DEAR DANGER

DEAR DANGER

TIFFANY LOWE

Illustrations by Charlene Mosley
Cover illustration by Charlene Mosley
Cover design by Dragan Bilic
Interior design by Mitch Green and Tiffany Lowe

First Edition

10 9 8 7 6 5 4 3 2 1

DEAR DANGER

To Danger
All my letters, all my words, all my
heart and soul.

I merely exist in his atmosphere and he
exists in mine,
we share the sky

and I'm in love with the star
that shines as bright
as I.

"We ate well and cheaply
and drank well and cheaply
and slept well and warm
together and loved each other."

— Ernest Hemingway,
A Moveable Feast

ONE
PROLOGUE

1.

It is both liberating
and all at once terrifying
that we belong
to nothing.

We are vast,
still partly unfathomable.

Some settle
with the salt and sand
to the bottom
of this dank, dark sea.
While others stay skyward –
not so much as a dip
in the waters –
and never land, never nest,
among the rest,
or her, or him.

She is still in the mist
of the relentless tide
floating haphazardly,
alternating between
being beaten by rocks at the bank,
and swallowing the swells.

She has a lot of love
no one has held
willingly.

She has never loved
anyone
who has held her.
She has never been held,
truly.

She loves to love those
who do not stay,
those who stray,
those who, even when close,
are so far away.

Or she would love to love them
if they would let her.

Her translucency depletes her.

But she is not yours,
or hers,
or his.

"I am only sometimes mine,"
she says.

She knows
no being has any
obligation to her.
And yet,
she hopes that one day
one of them sees her.

TWO
REUNITED

She called him Danger.

Dear Danger,

You have inquired about when we will see each other. Your tongue is sharp. Maybe it only seems so to me, as it shreds me without resistance and with minimal difficulty. Prior to the moment you lashed it at me so cunningly, calling me simply by my last name, I have been avoiding you — my apprehension is foolishly born of fear.

Well, dear Danger, I'm writing to say that you pose a good question that I am at last ready to answer.

When would be good for you?

Genuinely,
Red

Red
is what she called herself.

The color of her hair and
the fox
she saw herself as.

2.

He intimidated
the hell
out of her.

She was, on the other hand,
always attempting to be
accommodating.

His honesty was immediate.
His words were few,
but they were
truth.

He was brave,
so much braver than she.
And it excited her
in more ways than she could count
on her fingers
and her toes
and each last eyelash.

It was stimulating,
from those same appendages,
to each last sense that wanted to live
without fear of consequence.

Most of all,
it was so very attractive to her –
enchantingly
arousing.

Dear Danger,

To respond to your audacious suggestion that we meet this very night, it intrigues me that you are so forthcoming. I am attracted to your simplistic candor.

I would like to accept the invitation.
Where should we meet?

Genuinely,
Red

3.

He lived in Dallas at the time.

She aimed to impress him,
because he was so very impressive
to her.
Consequently, she said
she knew Dallas
well.
well,
she didn't.

She had, in fact, lived around it
her entire life
and spent many years of her girlhood
in Deep Ellum,
sneaking into music venues
before she was old enough to.

Meaning, she only knew
particular parts.
Parts that happened to be
different from
the parts
that he knew.

They were deciding
which bar that would be
the setting of
their long awaited rendezvous
and he said,

"What about Lakewood Landing?"

A bar that she had
never
been to before
or even
heard of.

She quickly looked it up,
without telling him,
and told him,
nonchalantly,
"That sounds good."

She shaved her legs
in the bathroom
at work,

then got lost
three times
on the way.

Cravings
are your body's way
of telling you what you
require
to survive.

Mine usually tells me
I will no longer exist
unless I find someone
to intimately know
like I know
myself.

And I haven't found them
yet.

4.

She hesitated outside
with her thoughts and affirmations:

You are elegant and alluring.
You are worthy and deserving.
You are much greater than the sum of
whatever happens here.

She was unsure about his, but
her confidence existed in years
of her own verification.

Her hands trembled as she
approached him inside –
standing at the bar, alone.
She begged her voice not to follow
in trembling.

Her first words to him:
"How was your day?"
Her nerves omitted her hello.

He looked at her, beer in his hand,
affirming his own self-assurance
with fixed eye contact,
and replied,
"Peachy."

He was unintentionally
captivating.

Dear Danger,

I'm scribbling this on the back of an old receipt in my purse, while sitting on a wooden bench outside Lakewood Landing. Your beer is making a condensation ring on the wood. You're in the restroom.

I'm writing to remember the way your voice vi-brated into my being on a low frequency that seemed to come from another time and place entirely. Speaking all this time, just waiting for anyone to hear it. And now I have, and it's all I want to listen to.

Genuinely,
Red

5.

She asked if he remembered
how they met.
He didn't,
but she did.

He had never said a word,
but he spoke to her
in song.

She even remembered
which song.

She didn't remember
what he was wearing
or what his hair looked like
back then.

It had been eleven years,
but she did remember that

tiny Chicago apartment
and how she had ill-advisedly
come to visit his roommate,
who was also an actor
like him,
and how his roommate wasn't home
the entire week
she was there, but
he was. he was there
with his guitar on his lap.

And now, there he was,
after so many seasons had
passed through them
and aged them,

smoking American Spirit
on that patio
in Dallas
with her.

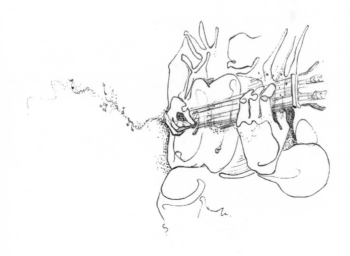

6.

Back in Chicago,
eleven years prior,
he had lured her in
from the bedroom
that she had been hiding away in,
awaiting a man
who never appeared,
like a pied piper.

She heard the melody
and she followed it
to him.

She sat beside him
while he strummed
the strings.
She observed,
in silence.

While she settled in,
vines wrapped about her legs,
stems on stems,
and cloaked her
in a way that felt both restricting
and reassuring –
immobile, but embraced.

He sang a John Mayer song
called Sucker.

When he finished,
the vines shriveled up
and fell at her feet,
and she walked away.

Just like that.

A spell cast
for what, at first,
seemed to last merely

three minutes,
undoubtedly
persisted for over a
decade.

Once upon another time
my fingers ached
down to the bone
from all the pretty words I wrote
and then I searched for them
again and again
in eyes and hands and skin
of all the women and men
and here they are, finally.

Here they are again.

Dear Danger,

This one is on an old bank deposit slip. You went to the restroom again. It's starting to get darker.

You should know, I had stowed away in my suitcase, since that Chicago trip in July of 2004, a retentive heat at the mere mention of your name. And I think, because of that, because of this little box filled with such fond-ness that I kept tucked away clandestinely, I was fated to fall in love with you from this very moment. This moment right here.

I was ignorant to the dormancy, looming to erupt. I carried the box with me into this bar in my pocket and it opened instinctively to the sound of your voice, consuming me in a nostalgia-induced stupor. It was a seduction by reminiscence.

Years ago, your gravity wasn't determined to keep me, our energy wasn't ready, but my trajectory made its way back to you.

And this time, your gravity is inescapable.

Genuinely,
Red

7.

They talked about their view
of the impending horizon,
on existence, and relations:
hookups, and breakups.

He told her she perceived things
optimistically.

She asked him,
"Is there
any other way
to see?"

He said,
"There are two, or three."

He explained that there was
pessimism and optimism,
and him:
a realist.

She said,
"There's at least one more."
because she, herself, was
an idealist.

He saw things as they were,
she saw them as they
could be.

The idealist in her
admired
the realist in him.

But on nights like
that

she was
so much closer
to
optimistic.

8.

It is probable that
the whiskey
did more talking
than she did,
but then it was dark
and their stomachs took over
the conversation.

He told her
he was going to eat
regardless
of her.

He said,
"We have options."

He listed them
in order from
least favorite to
favorite
personal preference.

Fast food drive-thru
and eat in his car.
Sit down at a restaurant
and chat some more.
Go to a grocery store,
buy fresh food,
and make it back
at his apartment.

It was up to her.

And she knew what he was asking
was so much more than
what food thy were going to eat.

What was really up to her
was where they were going to eat it.

She weighed the options
hastily
along with the
last three hours of conversation
and the
last three glasses of Jack.

and, she simply said,
"Lets go."

And with her eyes,
rather than her words,

She said, more than simply,
"Take me."

Dear Danger,

I'm in the bar bathroom before we take off. Toilet paper is all I could find, so this might be hard to read.

There is something familiar and easy about being in your presence. You scare me. But I am grateful to be scared, to feel greatly.

I have always been a floating pin, waiting to be dropped, and in this bar with you, I have finally been affixed to a point.

And now, it's time to go.

Genuinely,
Red

9.

They roamed up and down
the aisles at the grocery store:
grazing,
seeking sustenance.

When they got
to the frozen section,
she shivered
on purpose
to see what he would do.

He pulled her into him
instinctively
and wrapped his jacket
around them both,

and she'd never felt
so warm
in all her life.

1 0.

After very little debate
on her part –
remember,
always attempting to be
accommodating
– they settled on a chicken pizza
to bake at his apartment.

While the oven was pre-heating
they walked out
on the patio balcony
for him to smoke a cigarette
that he didn't smoke.

He had told her about
that balcony
on the bar patio earlier
that evening:

it looked like a forest;
a wilderness preserved
just for them,
in his own backyard.

They stood in silence,
his arm brushed hers,
she could hear him breathing.

She looked at him,
so she could file away
the way he looked
in the moonlight,

but at the same time
that her head turned
his firm hands were on her face
and entangled in her hair
and his lips
were on hers
before she had a chance
to breathe.

And briefly,
while her tongue
was getting acquainted
with his,
she forgot how to.

Dear Danger,

I found an old concert ticket stub in my wallet to pen this on while I sit on your couch as you are waiting for the pizza to finish.

I'm a mixed bag, filled with a miscellaneous assortment of confusion. Can you see it or could you taste it somehow? Do you know that I am conflicted with every passing glance (and kiss)?

I can hear my father's voice in my head: "why buy the cow, when you can get the milk for free?"

But I am no cow, nor property, nor wanting to be owned — merely loved — and there is no prerequisite for that.

I feel the years burdening me, gradually com-pressing and decimating any semblance of patience that I had.

It is far beyond sexual — an all encompassing magnetism.

I want to feel you and to know you once and for all.

Genuinely,
Red

1 1.

She was fascinated
with his hands
and how,
from the first time
they touched her,

they held her
as if the mere purpose
for them
were belonging
to her body.

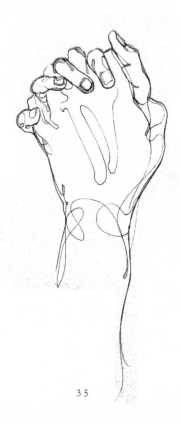

Dear Danger,

Thank you for letting me borrow a sheet of paper you tore out of one of your journals while we watch a movie and eat our pizza.

I don't know your story — other than you keep notes in journals. I know I have time to learn and it doesn't really matter to me yet. All I can see is the story we are beginning. And all these letters to you that are collecting in my purse after just a few hours together.

And I believe, intuitively, that I was part of your story before I even knew it, before I even knew you. But finally, we are consciously be-ginning.

And if you want to know my story, it's that I don't believe in much anymore. I've lost my faith in vows and eternity. I've lost the bricks in all the foundations I've ever built. I've lost my way, but I've found you. And, from the first drink on the patio at Lakewood Landing, I knew I believed in you, for now. For now, for now is all we have.

The real story is: I just want someone to see me.

Genuinely,
Red

1 2.

He was renting a room
at his actor friend's apartment,
as struggling artists do,
and his room was,
consequently, his friend's study
with just a desk
and a sleeping bag
and some blankets
on the floor.

She noticed quickly
that he was not
making it a priority
to find a place
to hang his hat,

rather he was
fulfilling the need
to have a roof,
and maybe,
she hoped,
a place to bring
her.

1 3.

He kept repeating to her,
"open your eyes"
as they made love
for the first time.

She was used to not only
shutting her own tight,
but at any peak
she would see
eyelids
staring back at her.

But not with him.

It's hard to train
your brain
to do something
you've never done –
even as simple as
keeping your eyes open
while being intimate.

But she did.

She shared an experience
rather than
a selfish taking
from only one party,
or maybe both,
of only a physical satisfaction.

Instead there was an
intangible, inner
devouring.

That night
he opened more than
just
her eyes.

1 4.

They fell asleep on his couch
with all their clothes
(back)
on
after watching two more movies
back-to-back.

Though, frame by frame,
she was unable to focus
on the films
and consciously had to keep
making herself pay attention
to the screen
rather than him

and his waves and waves
of dark corkscrew curls,
and his thick rimmed glasses
he only wore
when it was necessary.

And lord, when he
looked at her
from over them
it was a wonder
she could pay
any attention
at all.

1 5.

He drove her back to her car
the next morning
and she was complaining,

"Today is going to drag,
drag,
drag,
on and on and on."

She dreaded responsibilities,
She dreaded being present,
She dreaded doing anything at all,
aside from wasting away with him
all day.

He said,
"It is a beautiful day."
As he motioned to
the blazing, rising sun.
"Today is going to be
wonderful."

She said,
"Look who's being
optimistic
now."

1 6.

She carried him with her that day in
her hair and in her skin
and she could smell him
when she breathed,
and when she moved,
and in the wind.

And every day after,
she wrote him letters
each time
he came to her.

THREE
UNDEFINED

Dear Danger,

I have discovered, in you, someone that I don't aim to alter, that I don't feel entitled to, that I only want to savor.

If I am to take anything, anything at all, it will be knowledge and development.

That somehow feels precious and delicate but resilient and indestructible all at once.

Like dragonfly wings.

Genuinely,
Red

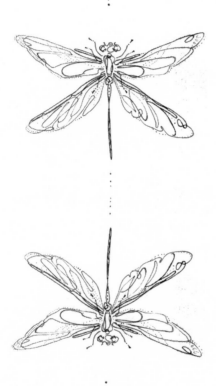

1 7.

Lines were never drawn
and she got accustomed to
the sparse communication
they had about
the non-existent
but ever-present
word –
"us."

1 8.

She wasn't overly concerned
or troubled.
But she got insecure at times.
After all, no matter how separate
she prided herself to be,
her vacillating anxieties
reminded her
that she wasn't.

He was, specifically,
something she didn't want
to fuck up.

But she waited,
and she was not normally patient.

She waited,
Because she was in no hurry.

She knew already –
after their single night together
– that there would be
plenty more,
plenty to follow,

plenty nights
where there was
only enough light
to see his face.

1 9.

She had dated an actor
before –
the reason she had met Danger.
She called him Chicago,
since that's the city he left her for.

She knew her role in Chicago's life.
She knew she made it
to every show,
front row.

But she was completely unsure
of her role with Danger.
They were lacking a script,
but she was grateful for that.
No characters,
no lines,
just a raw sincerity.

But it left her wondering.

He was playing Jesus
in a theater musical
when they began.
And she didn't see the show,
though she had wanted to.

But she was proud of him
and she was happy for him
just the same.

Dear Danger,

I tend to ponder often on an explanation behind the decade-long persistent grip I kept on him — as a concept. Was it you? I assume that sounds positively preposterous.

But, I speculate that everyone's energy, when they're around someone enough, can rub off a tiny bit.

So, it was like residuals of you were on him, and I sensed you on him.

When I was rightly pulled to you the entire time and he was this distracting static microfiber that our lint was clinging to.

And I want so much more than that.

Genuinely,
Red

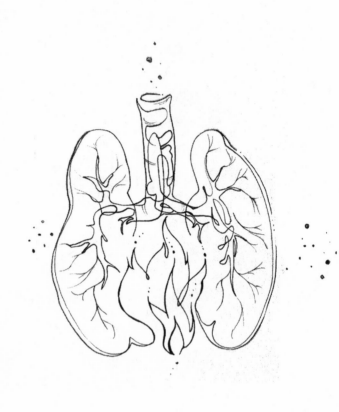

Dear Danger,

Do you remember how that first night, on the patio balcony, you told me that you are allergic to everything?

Immediately following that night, my chest has been ignited from the inside and my lungs refuse to take a full breath.

I am amused at the fact, my dear Danger, that falling for you has been like my own allergic reaction to love.

And what I had presumed to be fear of you when we first got reacquainted, the burn I felt and feel ever stronger now, is really my soul internally telling me – yelling at me – that it recognizes yours.

And I believe they have been waiting to meet again.

Genuinely,
Red

2 0.

A piece of clothing left
as gifts
for each step
on the way upstairs.

Their limbs entwined,
directly on the carpet.
No inch of skin left untouched.

He grabbed her hips, flipped
her onto her knees swift,
faced her towards
the full length mirror
hanging from the closet door,
entered her from behind, and
brushed her hair from her face.

His hand
wrapped around her neck,
his lips
pressed to her ear,
he coaxed her eyes open,
as he previously mastered with
her legs.

From deep within her
he urged her to look,

"Look at how sexy you are."

He made her
confront her own beauty,
naked, exposed in her entirety,
look herself in the eyes
and see
herself.

And he was right,
she thought,
he was right.

Dear Danger,

I am in love with the parts of you that leak out unexpectedly: like when you slip and call me baby. And how when we make love is the only time you call me by my first name, and I don't think anything I've ever heard before has ever sounded as sweet.

I know it is incidentally, accidentally.

And incidentally, accidentally, I answer to it like it is on purpose.

And incidentally, accidentally, I enjoy it.

And incidentally, accidentally, I am properly falling in love with more than just the parts of you that leak out unexpectedly – incidentally, accidentally.

Genuinely (on purpose),
Red

2 1.

They didn't chat much
between seeing each other.
And she was trying desperately not to.

So, she didn't get many messages
from him,
but she received one that said
he would be out of town
for a month
filming a movie in Louisiana,
but he hoped
they would see each other
when he got back in town.

She was relieved to see
that he also had
uncertainty.

Dear Danger,

You boil my insides.
Overflowing,
I disperse as merely steam and air in time.

Teach me,
I can learn
how to simmer slowly.

(No, I can't.)

Genuinely,
Red

22.

While he was gone
they started a new routine
of communication
by sending each other
videos and photographs
to showcase
how much they
missed each other.

Parallel lines running
concurrently:
less intimate,
yet more exposed.

2 3.

They had discussed her writing
and she mentioned,

"When I'm out
I like to save notes
in my phone,
you know, just
things that I'm thinking or feeling."

He said that he liked to keep it
old school
and write in a notebook –
pen on paper.

She remembered
his notebooks at his apartment
and she was fascinated.
She hadn't done that since
she was a teenager.
She hadn't much thought about it,
and then, she thought,
she should have.

She had felt for years that
her mind was clogged:
a congested drain
filled with so much
dead skin, hair, vile collections
of the past
stopped up, collected,

retaining it all.

And that was who
she assumed
she would always be:
the girl with her stories trapped
in her head.

Later that day,
she sent him words she had
jotted down
in her notes
on her phone,
and he called her:

A writer.
(That meant everything.)

After she had sent him several,
what she considered notes,
what she believed were
meaningless thoughts,
he asked her if she had sent out
her work.

She asked,
"What do you mean?
My notes?"

He said, "No,
that's poetry."

2 4.

It was weeks later,
while he was filming
the movie in Louisiana,
she was sitting in her room
thinking about what he said
when she dug through boxes
and found one of her
many gifted,
and empty,
never used,
notebooks.

She asked him to give her
an album recommendation
to listen to while she wrote.

"Wreck me," she told him.

And she used his last name,
like he'd always done with her.

And he did.
He wrecked her.

She listened to the album
he suggested,
Ryan Adams, self-titled,
on repeat
while she wrote through
the entirety
of the notebook
in one night.

And then she plowed through
his entire discography.

It was more
than music.

That was the night that
the clog in the drain
in her brain,
and all the words that were trapped,
and most of all
she,
came undone.

Dear Danger,

I dressed as a last minute flapper for Halloween. I bought the costume in a clearance rack that looked like it had been hit by a tornado. It was two sizes too big.

I slipped it on in the car with some opaque tights, a sequined feather headband, and some red lipstick, and went out with friends. We ended up at a club that was packed shoulder-to-shoulder. You wouldn't have enjoyed it at all.

I took my tights off in the bathroom, because they made me feel juvenile, and kept them in my purse. Thank you for telling me I looked pretty when I sent you a photo of me after a few drinks. I didn't feel very pretty. A man had just shoved me to get his drinks a minute quicker, like he didn't even see me there at all. But the band was playing cover songs that everyone knew. I suppose that was amusing.

I got invited to an after party by Thor and Hawkeye, but I went home instead and thought about how I wished I had been playing dress up with you.

Genuinely,
Red

2 5.

As soon as he got back
she was at his door.

She knew she might not be
the only face he'd see,
or body he would hold,
or lips he would kiss,
but she knew
she was the most
important.

The prominence of
time apart
is the reconvening.

2 6.

The second or third time
that they made love,
after he got back
from Louisiana,
he questioned her
on if she had been satisfied
completely yet
with him
and she told the truth:

She had not experienced it
ever
before him.
No man had cared enough
to make her believe
that she even could.
If they cared more than
none at all
they would get her there before,
then the actual act
was more about getting him there.

That was all sex had been to her
up until that point:
getting a man to climax
(and hopefully to love her.)

He insisted that she could,
and that they would try
all night.

2 7.

They sat
facing each other –
her on top
of him,
her legs wrapped
tight
around his back –
and they did try
all night.

She exerted
every effort
with his forehead
against hers,
looking her
right in the eyes,
kissing her
a hundred times.

The light
that he had ignited
was spreading
throughout her body,
settling most of the energy
right between her legs,
where they were joined
as one,

challenging
the light

in him
to meet hers there
in the middle.

And it did.

The building
of electricity
was gradual that night.
They had to convince
their flames
that it was safe
to come out
and play.

She closed her eyes
when she got close
and she could see
their souls
stripped bare,
and when she
opened them again
she could still see them
– ever so briefly,
as they collided

and they were showered
in all the stars
that lived and died
so that very moment
could arrive.

Dear Danger,

You always smell like coconuts. Every time I smell coconuts, for the rest of my life, I'll think of you. Like paradise.

You know, I think we create love. Do you think that's possible? We quite literally create it as we're making it, but we are so close that it can't breathe.

We recreate it. Every time.

And every single time I am willing to give the breathe from my own lungs just so it can live.

Genuinely,
Red

Dear Danger,

You're always playing sounds of rain as we sleep.

Now, when it rains, I wander as I'm drifting off – and it is there that you seep. You're the water droplets on my window. Condensation that gathers, creating waves on me, in me. The thunder builds inside to a screaming echo that never subsides.

And when I am awake on quiet, cloudless nights, wrapped in only sheets, I beg and beg for rain.

Genuinely,
Red

2 8.

Humanity,
and society,
doubted them,
and made her
doubt them
too.

Their voices were so loud
when they were in unison.

She would want
more
from him,
because she was told
she should
want more
so often
that she would be
convinced they were
right.

Even though
she was the only one
other than him
that their relationship
entailed,
they had this way
of inserting themselves
like weeds

that she had to actively
be picking
or they would drop
more seeds
that would grow
more weeds
that would grow roots.

She would pick them
one by one,
but sometimes

she would miss one.

Dear Danger,

When you play music when we make love, the artists and the songs weave their lyrics and their tunes through my life — stitched together like a quilt.

I hear them and they cover me so cozily. The nights that you can't hold me, I'm wrapped up in melodies.

Genuinely,
Red

2 9.

They were out
on his patio balcony
and he saw
something magnificent
in the sky
among the trees
around them.

His eyes lit up
like she had never seen
and he told her something
he said only she knew

and to this day,
she's the only one who will know,

and that
on days like that
good things happened
and she wanted desperately
for him to think
that the good thing
could possibly just
be her.

Dear Danger,

The more I get to know you, the more you tell me about her. The only one that ever really mattered before now.

And the way you talk about her, with such hatred, makes me wonder how much you still love her. A therapist once told me that the opposite of love is not hate, it is indifference.

I wonder if you miss her, all the time. Both if you miss her all the time, and I wonder all the time.

Secretively,
Red

3 0.

She folded that one
into quarters
and placed it in a drawer
where she kept all her letters
that she either
wouldn't dare
or
couldn't bare
to give to him.

3 1.

She would always be jealous
of the girl he loved,
when he still knew how to,
when he still wanted to,
when he still believed he could
love someone
the way he loved her.

She would always wish
they met
before she made him regret,
before she made him resent,
before she made him
forget.

She would always wish
he knew
she was worth
remembering for

and
she would always be jealous.

People are a precipice
and with you I am hesitant.

But with all the strength I feign,
I am holding back a freight train.

FOUR
BE HERE NOW

3 2.

He drove her to a dive bar.
They had been there before but
that night was
karaoke night.
It was December and there were
Christmas lights
hanging from the ceiling.
Old people were singing
old country songs.
He asked her
if she was going to sing
and when she said no
he sang without her.

Great Balls Of Fire.

She paid attention to
every
single
word.

She had heard the song before, but
it sounded different that time.
She was giggling
and smiling.
She couldn't take her eyes off him
except to glimpse around
to catch a peek at
the old people dancing
and then to
listen to them clap
when it was over
and tell him how
marvelous
he was.

She, admittedly,
also glanced around to see
if they all saw him kiss her
as he returned to their table.

Listening to him sing
Great Balls of Fire
in that little bar
was when she knew.
She knew he was who
she would measure
every single man up to
from that moment on.

She knew
he was it.

He was
it.

3 3.

They had sex in his car that night,
and again on the floor
in the living room
when they got back.

The weight of the night
started to feel
so heavy,
and her lungs were collapsing
in her chest.

They didn't talk
about that night
ever again,
but he held her close to him,
so close, he held her
so close, skin on skin
and he told her,
"Be with me.
Be here now."

And no matter
how many times he calmed her
he somehow believed
he was not comforting.

Regardless,
she replayed that night
in her head
on a loop
all the time.
When her anxiety took over
and she forgot how to breathe,
she heard his voice
telling her,

"Be here.
Be here now."

Dear Danger,

People think you love to be loved. It's in the broken hearted songs and poetry and movies and media. I think I've found the secret to not feeling betrayed and broken-hearted. It is to stop looking at anyone like they owe you anything.

I think we should all love whole humans, because we love them and for no other reason. We should love them, because of who they are — beautiful and alive. We should love them because they changed our lives simply by being in them.

We should love them, love them, and not ask them to love us back, so when if they do or if they don't it doesn't even matter at all.

Because loving someone for them is the grandest achievement of the heart.

Genuinely,
Red

3 4.

One night
when she got to his apartment
he was out on the patio,
which he usually was,
and sometimes his roommate
was there, but
this time it was someone else.
He introduced her
and the new person
said her name out loud
with exclamation,

"Tiffany!"

Like he knew that name,
like he had heard it before
from Danger
and he had been waiting
to meet her.
It was the first time
she was aware of him
maybe
telling other people
about her.
The conversations that night
consisted of strippers
and a dominatrix
and sex parties.
and
laughter.

3 5.

The next morning,
before she left,
her goodbye kiss
lingered longer than usual
on his lips.

He held her close,
looked into her eyes
as if he was searching for
what to do next.

They had made love
twice
already that morning.

When he finally spoke,
he said,
"Okay,
one more time."

As he whisked her away
and carried her up the stairs
into that little office room
and took her right there
on the desk.

Dear Danger,

I always used to say that you never love again like before you were hurt, like your first love, before you had your heart broken.

I still think that's true.

When I first met you I was selfishly loving someone that I thought was my first love and he broke me in every way you can break someone. And until you and I met again, over a decade later, I had never loved again, though I tried, and I failed, and I tried, and broke myself more than he'd ever broken me, so that I could put myself back together on my own. And by the time you came back around I was prepared to never love the same way that I had before.

I was prepared to love you better.

Genuinely,
Red

3 6.

She stayed with him
the week before Christmas.
He had a tiny tree on a table
with gifts collected underneath.
She had been there for two days
before he handed her
two of the gifts wrapped in
construction paper.

He said,
"In case I don't see you."

She was grateful, but surprised.

She said, "Thank you" meekly,
put them both in her purse
and didn't touch them again.
She hadn't planned to get him
anything,
because she tended to go overboard
and care
too much,
and she wasn't aware he cared
at all.

About Christmas,
or about
her.

She started to feel anxious
about sticking around too long.
The holidays created a constant
panic
in her.
And being around him
during the holidays
felt tremendous.

She stayed one more day,
they saw the new Star Wars movie
in the theater,
they smoked weed
outside in the parking lot
before
and after
the movie,

and she went home.

3 7.

She unwrapped them that night
and cried.

He got her two notebooks.

As a writer
she had been gifted
many
over the years.
She thought it was still
a sweet thought,
but then she opened one up
to look inside.

He had handwritten
his favorite poems
in the first few pages.

It was the most
genuine,
thoughtful
gift
she had ever received.

And the first tears
she'd cried over a man
in a long while,
were joyous ones.

3 8.

He was sick on Christmas day,
so she brought him a box of goodies
to unwrap while he was
laid up
in bed
and left it on his doorstep:
a nice bottle of whiskey
and cans of soup
for his cold,
a homemade chocolate pecan pie
that she baked herself
(she had never baked a pie before),
and a letter and a poem.
She didn't get to see his face
when he opened them,
but he hadn't seen hers
when she opened his to her.
It was only fitting, but

she hoped that his
lit up, despite his sickness,
as brilliantly
as hers had,

or,
maybe,
even more.

3 9.

She sang to herself
in the car on the way
back home,
an Amy Winehouse song,
Tears Dry On Their Own:

I don't know why I got so attached
It's my responsibility
And you don't owe nothing to me
But to walk away I have no capacity

And it was true.

He didn't owe anything to her,
and still
she could not
get enough.

Though her car drove away,
her heart stayed
in that little basket
right next
to the whiskey.

Dear Danger,

You possessing my thoughts is more powerful than anything I could give you materially.

Genuinely,
Red

4 0.

She showed up to his
newly rented room
with a basket filled with food.
Fresh made pasta and salads,
and a bottle of champagne.
They watched the clock change from
11:59 to 12:00,
he popped the cork,
took a swig straight from the bottle, and
kissed her hard
with bubbles still on his lips.
They made love on the wicker couch
that had cushions that wouldn't stay put,
with the sound of fireworks
in the Dallas sky for hours.
She made a resolution
to never forget the way
he felt
in that moment.

(Spoiler:
On the fourth of July
she sat in the sticky Texas heat
alone,
yet all she could feel
was a bright
cold
winter night.)

4 1.

She was drinking wine
out of a coffee mug one night
in January.
She had always mentioned
how much she liked
that particular mug
and how cool she thought it was.
It had a lightening bolt
that represented The Flash
on it.

He collected comic books.

But she was incapacitated
and being careless
with her thoughts
and knocked it
to the floor.

It shattered the instant it hit.

He saw the embarrassment
and shock on her face
immediately
and told her it was fine
and not to move.

But terror overcame her
and her sobs could not be
contained.

While cleaning it up
he reminded her
that stuff
was just that – stuff.
Stuff never meant
anything
to him,

but she did.

4 2.

In her hysteria
she told him
how a friend of hers
had told her that
she was fire —
like a gaseous,
burning star —
and she realized
that she was:
she was fire.
And he was the one
who had brought it
out of her.
He
of course
would take no credit
for this
and it began to frustrate her.

She said to him,
"When someone tells you
that you changed their life,
you can't tell them
that you didn't."

He said to her,
"Okay." Smiling,
"You're right."
He kissed her forehead,
"Thank you."

4 3.

The very next time she saw him
she gave him a new mug she bought
with him in mind that,
when hot liquid was poured into it,
revealed the Eye of Agamotto
from Doctor Strange,
who was his favorite
comic book character,
which he only mentioned to her
once,
but she remembered
everything.

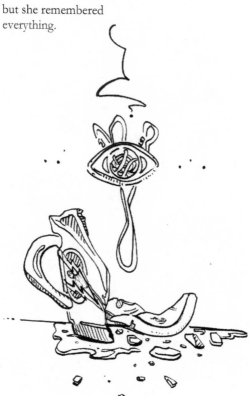

4 4.

One day,
out of – seemingly –
nowhere
he told her
it was time.
It was time for him
to go.

He had said it in passing before,
that he might want to move
to Los Angeles
to try his luck there.

To "roll the dice"
as he had put it,
from his favorite
Bukowski poem,
which was one of the poems
he scribbled in the first page
of the journal
that he gifted her
that last Christmas.

Lots of people
say lots of things,
but she should have known
that he would "go all the way."

And with those words,
"I'm going to
pack up,
and head West,"

she expanded
and exploded
like a dying star.

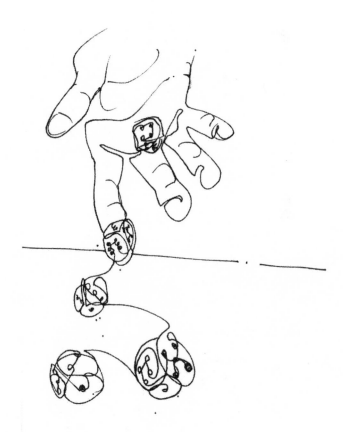

4 5.

She had always heard,
"actions speak
louder than words."

but to the girl
who paints
with the alphabet

words are deafening.

FIVE
AUSTIN

4 6.

After time to process,
the thought of him leaving
was never a thought
that destroyed her mind.
The thought of him leaving
was a pleasant one,
because she wanted
more
for him.

She told him,
"you are bigger
than here,
or me,
or us."

Though there was so much
more
that she wanted to say.
Instead
she let the words go,
she let him go.

She would sit on the floor
of the shower
and sing to herself:
songs she made up
with the words
she could never
speak to him.

First draft:

Dear Danger,

If all else fails, I love you. I know it isn't much but it's something. Most days, it is everything. So, go out there and find yourself, but if all else fails, I love you.

Love,
Tiffany

The one she gave to him:

Dear Danger,

All I want for you is to succeed. To be happy. To be more.

This is bittersweet for me: the realization that what I feel for you is so selfless and pure.

I didn't plan for you, or to feel that way for anyone, ever.

But I'm so glad.

If you take anything from me, take my belief. My belief in you and how you are infinite.

I'll miss you. More than you know.

Genuinely,

Red

4 7.

It was a simple, quick conversation:

Her: When will I see you again?
Him: Can you drive to Austin?
Her: When?
Him: Today?
Her: Yes.

She waited until 7:00pm,
to avoid traffic
on the 200 mile drive South,
but she didn't account for
construction
on I-35
in the dark.
And her low blood sugar
by Waco.
And her anxiety
that was worsened
exponentially
by Texas drivers.
But she made it there by 11:00pm,
and he was outside
on the porch,
smoking a cigarette
as she pulled up,
and when she saw his face
it was worth
every
bit.

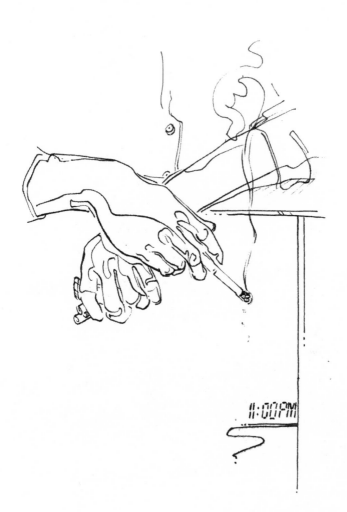

4 8.

She told her dad
on the phone
on the way,

"When he calls,
I don't drop everything…
I throw it
out of
a moving train."

4 9.

He was staying out in Austin
for a month before moving to LA
to help write a script with
a fellow artist.

He was staying at a house
with the fellow
and an older woman
who owned the house.

On the first night in Austin
they stayed up talking
with the fellow
and had one of those nights
where you learn so much
about human beings
just by being around them
and conversing.

The fellow thanked her
for some insight,
when she had listened to him
complain about other women
who kept asking too much
of him, from him:
"Never ask someone something
that you can't answer yourself."

And she continued to live
by that.

5 0.

He always had with him
this small notebook
and she had never asked
what was in it
or why.
She was big on privacy.
He was big on privacy.
They lived
copacetic
that way.
The fellow snatched it up one day
and he snatched it back
almost simultaneously.
The fellow asked what was
inside
and he said,
"Ideas
and thoughts
and shit."
The fellow shrugged
and walked away.
He looked at her, with a smile,
and put it in her hands.
It was a gesture
that she didn't take lightly,
as she returned it
immediately
back to his.

And she said to him,

"That's yours,
not mine.
That is private property.
Everyone has secret
safe places,
and I don't need to
invade yours
to feel important to you.

If you ever want to show me,
or tell me,
any little thing,
I'll devour every word,
but everyone deserves
their secret safe place.

That's yours,
not mine.
That you offered at all,
is all I need
to see."

5 1.

On the second night,
she had too much wine
and he was talking
about LA.
She kept trying to stay positive,
but instead
she kept walking away
pretending to use the bathroom,
where she went
to cry.

He finally realized
what was happening,
because she was never good at
hiding emotions
from her face,
and chased behind her.
The house only had
one bathroom
with two doors.
She made it to one,
but he made it to the other.

She collapsed into his arms
and cried
about how she would miss him
about how she was scared
she would never see him again
about how,
even through her tears,

she was still so happy.

She was happy to know him,
happy to love him,
happy to see him
live
and breathe
with her.

But the soul inside her
was ripping
in two.

He said,
"You are believing
that this is the end.
This is not the end.
We are
not over yet."

He held her,
and kissed her,
and made love to her,
as she continued to cry,
and she believed him.

She believed
there was more –
they were
more.

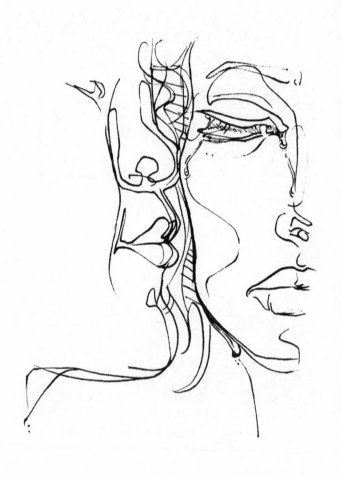

Dear Danger,

You're leaving the city,
you're not
leaving me.

And I love you
more than
I love us.

Goodbye for now,
Red

5 2.

She left Austin,
back to Dallas
in the rain,
but she couldn't tell.

She could hardly see –
through the windshield,
through her eyes.
It was water,
water,
all the same.

5 3.

They were somewhere
in between,
but at least
they were together there.

She would rather stay
in that limbo
forever
with him
than decide a path
and venture out
either way
and lose him.

5 4.

She met him
and a couple friends
at the first bar they met at,
from their first date
months before –
Lakewood Landing –
for a send off night.

They had some drinks,
some snacks,
some laughs.

She held tight to his leg
under the table,
because she knew soon
she would let him go.

5 5.

She got pulled over
after leaving the bar,
but the policeman just wanted
to tell her
that her headlights weren't on,
which was a good thing,
because she'd had a couple
whiskey and cokes.

He had a slight panic attack
on the way to the hotel.
They pulled over
while she waited for him to
take a breath,
like she knew
all too well.

When they got to the hotel
they couldn't check in,
because the reservation
was for the next night.

They sat in his car
and booked another hotel.

5 6.

When they got to the hotel
they were ready to
rip each other's clothes off –
which they did
and in their hurried mess
he fell off the bed
and they both laughed

and they both needed
to laugh
in that moment.

Dear Danger,

Too many times other people push for absolutes, they pressure to cater to how they feel personally, inconsiderately, and to change, and mold, those around them to their own convenience to make them more comfortable.

I never want that from you.

I don't care about being comfortable. I want you to be limitless, like the vast, expansive celestial being that I see withheld within you. Unchained, to pursue this earthly life for everything it has intended for you.

Genuinely,
Red

57.

He told her,
"every thought of you
is an inspiration."

The day he left
she kissed him goodbye
with a smile.

SIX
LOS ANGELES

Dear Danger,

Tell me, far away, about the sky
and all about the night.
Do they smile there,
and what about their eyes?
Tell me you're happy, far away
and tell me it's okay —
it's okay to miss you, far away.

Genuinely,
Red

5 8.

She missed him
so much.

Her soul burned
for him
so often
that she felt
her skin
melting right off.

Dear Danger,

I can't create sustainable energy to feed my happiness. I understand now why I overwhelm people. A person can not be your purpose and they can not be the reason why you feel purpose within yourself. I'm searching now to see it in myself, to feel it for myself. Most days I can not find one — a purpose.

I hope you have out there.

I've also realized, with all this time on my hands, that you can't look at other's life choices and take them personally or like they are happening to you.

I'm trying to keep living without you, to keep dreaming, and to keep writing.

But in every word, is you.

Genuinely,
Red

5 9.

He would send her pictures
of the mug she had bought him
with palm trees in the background
but they didn't talk much
other than that
and she was feeling
him slipping through her fingers
but being thankful
that she was touching him at all.

And every now and then
she would get
messages
about how lonely he was
out there.

She knew
he was trying to have a life
without her –
with someone else –
but she still hid her sadness from him,
and comforted him,
and told him
she hoped
he would find
better days
in the sun
among the palm trees.

Dear Danger,

I'm trying, in vain, to forget about you. To not need you. To not miss you all the time. Some nights are harder than others, but I've come to realize that some nights are most nights. Most nights are hard.

Yet, it kills me that you are not happy. I am fire, but for you I will be rain – calm your worries, ease your pain. I am lightning, as you are thunder. I will light up your sky, so you can navigate the night, as you keep rolling by. I will be the showers, for a moment, for you. Let it wash away, let it wash all away.

My darling Danger, you are the sun.

Genuinely,
A rainy day that you'll never get out there in Los Angeles.

6 0.

At night she was
particularly melancholy,
and missing him so,
she was out and about,
drinking with friends.

There wasn't enough whiskey
in the whole bar
to drown her soulache –
which was similar to heartache
but on a much grander scale –
when an old friend and lover
came through the door.

In her most vulnerable weakness,
after one or two more,
and bypassed small talk,
she asked to go home with him.

There she wrestled
her demons
in her old friend's bed
that she tried
so damned
to forget.

In the morning,
she awoke there,
feeling the same,
and tried again.

6 1.

Her old friend drove her home,
and they passed the house
she grew up in,
and the parking lot
where she learned to drive,
and they talked of a girl
he was seeing and quite fancied.
She wished him luck
and he wished her the same,
but she needed more than luck.
She needed him,
the one who was so far away.

And she wondered
if he was trying to forget her
just the same.

Dear Danger,

I dreamed of you – a dream so real. It was between asleep and awake. It felt more like reality than a dream. You were laying in bed shirtless, reading a book. You were just in underwear. You had your glasses on. I was already naked, like we had just been lounging about all day. I crawled up in the bed and laid with you, and I just said "hi". You smiled at me and looked at me over your glasses, like you do, and said "hi". And it sounded like you. You took your glasses off and laid your book down. You kissed me. And it tasted like you. I climbed on top of you while we kissed. I gripped you and guided you inside me myself, because I needed to feel you inside me. And it felt like you. Every detail. My hand on the back of your neck, your hair, your eyes, what you feel like inside me. Your skin on mine. You said my name, I said your name, we both came. That woke me up – breathless, sweating, shaking – because I really came. It made me so happy for a moment. The mind is a powerful thing. I've wanted you so bad since I woke up.

I wish you were here.

Breathlessly,
Red

6 2.

She felt like an animal
caged
inside her own body,
like she didn't belong
trapped inside of it.

Her soul
was
bursting
to get out
and to see him
again.

6 3.

She began to doubt
everything.

She hated that,
without him,
her rationality
ceased,
and her optimism
had left with him.

She failed to see
meaning
in even the tiniest of things,
but also the greatest.

Like living.

She made a point
to not make him her purpose
or to feel a purpose
because of him,
but she was unsuccessful
at finding one
on her own.

6 4.

The popular belief
of his friends
was that she was
such a poor girl –
a lost puppy
waiting for him.

That was enough
to enrage her.

She was not poor,
nor a puppy.

She was rich with potential
and she was
a goddamn
fox.

Dear Danger,

Contrary to popular belief, I don't need to be sleeping around or seeing others in order to be striving without you. I am not waiting for you. Or maybe I am.

Having you in my life is uplifting and empowering. You have always treated me as if I was capable and whole, since the very first day, and I love that.

What I don't love or appreciate is all the insinuations that I'm crying into my cheerios, kicking dirt, and sitting on my hands while you're away.

I'm working on myself. I might not always be perfect at it, and maybe even sometimes might lose myself completely, but I'm doing it, for the first time, and I'm doing it alone. That has been good for me.

This anger is not directed towards you, but I had to make sure that you knew. Our choices do not reflect or mirror others. Our perception of the choice is, in turn, our choice. My choices are my own. My choice to still love you is my own.

As passively as possible,
Red

6 5.

Time passed,
so slowly,
but it passed.

Then,
after two months,
that had felt like eternity,
he was coming home
to visit.

SEVEN

YOUR CHOICE

I was left
with an F. Scott Fitzgerald quote
about his wife
and what he fell in love with
about her
and also
your words
about wanting me
to be something
in the time apart.

I hope I was
something
enough.

6 6.

She got to the airport
an hour early
to pick him up,
and she didn't want to pay
to park her car,
so she drove around in circles
at the arrivals
and listened to
the same three songs
on repeat.

6 7.

She had gotten them
a hotel for the night,
and she was excited
to be the one
to provide
for once,
even if it was something
as simple
as a room
for them to lay in
together.

She had gotten them
a hotel for the night,
and none of the lamps worked,
and they couldn't find anything
to watch on the television,
and the liquid massage heart
she brought
was too hot, she thought
it would burn him,
and the food from the bar
was too cold, she thought
it might make him sick.
and she had brought
a bottle of wine
but forgot a corkscrew,

and the door to the bathroom
was a sliding slab of concrete
that rolled over his foot
when he closed it.

She had gotten them
a hotel for the night,
and she massaged his back
with her bare hands,
and they sat in the dark,
and they snacked on chips,
and they turned on the news
(which they both actually preferred),
and he asked the bar
to open her wine,

and he talked to her
more than he ever had.
and she felt closer to him,
more than she ever had.

And she was excited
to be the one
to provide
for once,
even if it was something
as simple
as a room
for them to lay in
together.

Dear Danger,

I have learned that some people misunderstand you. They do not see you, because you are honest.

People confuse being nice with being outwardly kind. Usually, it means having to lie to protect, and to preserve, peace.

But being nice is not about living easy.

The genuinely nicest thing you can give to another is your truth.

You taught me that.

So, in actuality, you are nice, because you are truth. Truth is always nice, even when it hurts.

Genuinely,
Red

6 8.

They ate at this small café
and she asked the old lady
for sweet tea,
but she told her,
"Honey, we only have tea.
you can sweeten it yourself."
They got his order wrong,
but the food was good,
and the people were frank,
but they were kind.
He looked for a movie
for them to see,
to pass the time,
but none were playing
that they could catch,
so they went to the mall
and walked around
holding hands
like a proper couple,
if only for an hour.

6 9.

She went with him
to a sound studio
where he re-did some of his lines
for the movie he had filmed
in Louisiana.

She got to watch the scenes
in another room
while he was in the sound booth.

She felt so special
even being there
and she loved
getting the opportunity
to watch him work
for the first time.

7 0.

They stopped by
a stoner friend's house
to get some weed
and when they arrived
he motioned for her
to jump on his back,
where she rode all the way
to his stoner friend's door
as they laughed.

And then they smoked
and laughed
some more.

7 1.

They drove back to Austin
together
and the entire three hours
they barely said a word.

And she thought of the scene
in Pulp Fiction
where Mia says,

"That's when you know
you've found somebody
really special.
When you can just
shut the fuck up
for a minute
and comfortably share
silence."

7 2.

That night
after they got to Austin,
she spilled his beer
on the porch
and then spilled her red wine
on her favorite jeans.

He smiled at her
and kissed her,
and reminded her,
"It's just stuff."
like he always did.

Her lips turned purple
when she drank red wine
and she would get
overly sensitive,
but he got her
out of those jeans
before she could cry about it
and made sure she went to bed
well loved
(twice).

She stayed with him in Austin
for a week.
That was
her favorite night.

7 3.

He had these little quirks
that week in Austin.
It was the longest time
they had spent together
at one time,
and she was seeing parts of him
that she hadn't seen before.

Like sometimes
after he kissed her
he would pretend to bite
her entire face.
and her laugh
would echo
and fill
the entire house.

Or they would make eye contact
from across the room
and he would wink at her
and make her entire body
tingle.

Or sometimes she would catch him
smiling
this impossibly beautiful smile
that took over his face
and crinkled
all the way
up to his eyes.

This impossibly beautiful smile
that made her ache
and she knew that her reason
for being in his life
was to make him smile
like that.

7 4.

He knew exactly
who he was,
and he was
unapologetically him.

He lived honestly
and he pushed her
to do the same.
She wasn't even aware
of who
her true self was
until him.

And after she did
know her,
she loved her.

7 5.

He had left to Dallas
early in the morning
and she woke up to words
on the mirror:
"The journey is your choice."

She wasn't sure if he wrote it,
or the fellow or the woman had,
but she knew
that she would take those words
with her back to Dallas.

The journey was
her choice.

EIGHT
YOU AND ME

Dear Danger,

I am still observing, attempting to utilize my space in a place where every being is separate. Trying to make sense of how I can still be me while loving you.

It's a perpetual endeavor, my dear Danger. Sustaining an authentic, unbroken version of myself while appreciating this undeniable attachment to you.

But I will keep at it. I will keep reconciling this all-encompassing love with my need to be no one's but my own.

Apologetically,
Red

Their choices do not reflect,

or mirror,

you.

Your perception of the choice is,

in turn,

your choice.

When you feel
completely content,
fulfilled, happy,
bottle it.
Because you will forget,
for whatever reasons,
you will forget.
and when you do,
you can take that bottle
to your lips,
and remember.
Sip it, savor it,
taste that smile
you stored away,

and
remember.

7 6.

It had been a couple weeks
since she had seen him,
since the trip to Austin,

and he said to her,
"I want to see you,
but I want it to be right,
like it has always been
with us,
like the whole world
doesn't exist
past us."

7 7.

She came to pick him up
to take him to the airport
to head out
to New York,
and met his dad
and grandmother.

He introduced her
as his friend,
but she still
felt like it was a
big deal.

After all,
he was her friend.
He was
her very best
friend.

7 8.

They stopped at a bar
on the way to the airport
and drank Bloody Mary's.
They talked about how
little understanding
and how
much questioning
their friends had
of their relationship.

It was not bound by
their rules
and because of that
it was not valid.
But they lived
by a quote
from one of their
favorite series,
Game Of Thrones,

"It's you and me
that matters
to me and you."

7 9.

That day she realized
she didn't
cry
about him
anymore.

You are

so

much

more

than the sorting

and ranking

of your relationships.

Humans

weren't meant to be

consisting of

merely pieces

of other humans.

We are all

completely free

from each other,

floating in a space

meant only

for ourselves.

8 0.

She kept the pack of cigarettes
he left in her car
when she dropped him at the airport.
They were menthol,
which he never smoked, but
she kept them anyway.
She smoked one, then
put the pack away
in the drawer
that had all the letters
she never gave to him.

Dear Danger,

I was thinking today about how no one is required or obligated to love you simply because you love them. And how that is one of the hardest things for humans to comprehend.

I know it has been hard for me. But that you choose me, consistently and consciously, has to be enough for me. You do not owe me any more than that and my love should not have any precursors for it to exist for you.

Your love could very well be different than what I've been told love is.

And your love could very well be the only love I can stand.

Genuinely,
Red

8 1.

He held her
without keeping her.
He told her,
"You are never a commodity."

So many hands, before his,
attempted to seize her,
incapacitate her,
treated her
unfairly.
She felt inadequate, and incomplete,
incapable of decision making,
possessing little opportunity,
endlessly trying to be
more.

She forgot her own capability.

She was sacrificing.
She, at times unwillingly,
hollowed in their hands.
She walked away,
emptier than before.

His hands remained open
and his words filled her,
overflowing
overflowing
overflowing.

She was free to leave,
and she wasn't trying to be
more
any longer.
He unprecedentedly,
added to who she already was,
and reminded her
of her full capacity.

He held her
without keeping her,
but he helped her
shine
in all her glory.

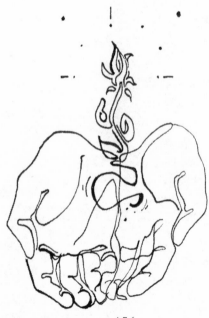

8 2.

He asked her
to go camping with him,
since it had been weeks again
since they'd seen each other,
at a campsite
he was filming at.

But all the cabins were either
booked out
or flooded
from the recent rains.

So, they improvised.

They stopped for a cheap beer
(she didn't drink beer)
at a dive bar
that was mostly just
a couple old men
gabbing
like old women.

Then, their next stop was
for gas station food.

Lastly, a cheap hotel
for the love
they were needing
from each other.

8 3.

On nights such as those,
she tried to look from the outside
in,
and see them objectively.
To figure out
if she was being delusional,
and if she would look back
and think any differently
than she did then.

NINE
BEATNIK

8 4.

She called him Beatnik,
because he didn't like
to be called Hipster.

But he was,
complete with glasses and beard.
He wore skin tight jean shorts
that were probably fair trade
and organic
that had a recycle symbol patch
on the thigh.
He traveled the world,
and climbed mountains,
and liked to slackline
out in the woods by the river
behind his parent's house.
He listened to mostly indie music
she'd never heard of,
but he also liked Johnny Cash.
(Johnny Cash
reminded her of Danger –
Folsom Prison Blues.)
He liked beer and coffee,
but didn't mind if it was cheap.
He liked to get tattoos
that didn't really mean
anything at all
to him.
And he was a friend
at the right time.

8 5.

She started dating Beatnik
while Danger was off
in New York,
or wherever he was,
he wouldn't talk to her much
and she was stale
from not knowing.

She wanted to feel
fresh and new
again.

Before Danger left,
he'd told her,
"When I get back
we'll do something special,
something big,
I promise."

And she only stewed on that
for two days.

Before words
couldn't satisfy her
anymore.

8 6.

While out drinking with friend's
on Cinco de Mayo,
after going to a funeral for a boy
younger than her
who overdosed on heroin,
she texted Beatnik
and asked him to come out.

He had been trying to date her
for years, since they met,
and she thought she would
give him a try,
give normal a try,
give what society
wanted so badly for her
a try.

8 7.

That night they kissed
for the first time
out in front of the pub
and strangers whistled at them
like they were happy for them
and they laughed.

They stowed away
to a hotel nearby,
and she didn't feel excitement
as much as she felt guilt
in her climax.
An orgasm could not
suffice,
when she had gotten so much
more
from Danger.

8 8.

She stayed with him
almost every day
the next two weeks.

He fit in seamlessly with her friends,
they drank beer together,
and went to music shows,
and talked liked they'd known him
the whole time.
Her dad liked him,
because he picked her up,
and he took her out on dates,
and he offered to change the oil
in her car.
He said all the right things,
and he wanted a family.

Every night she spent
with him
she would steal away
to the restroom
to cry.

He was only perfect
in theory.

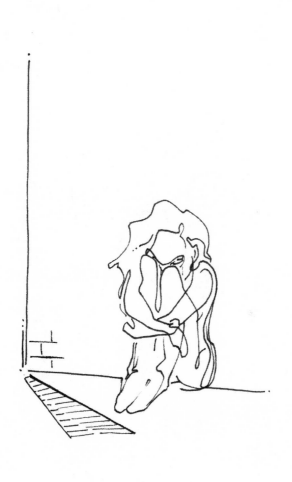

8 9.

Beatnik took photos,
really beautiful photos,
of all the places he saw
and the people he met.
He took photos of her –
sometimes planned,
out by the airport
where the wind could
blow her hair,
and sometimes impromptu,
in his bed, in just his shirt,
or in only underwear
while she put on her makeup
in the morning.

Beatnik was kind to her.

But he didn't fit
inside her
quite the same.

He didn't fit
at all.

Dear Beatnik,

I know that I'm crazy. Thank you for making me feel a little less so and a little more loved.

For Now,
Red

90.

That was the only letter
that she ever wrote to him.
She wasn't very kind
in return.

Dear Danger,

He sometimes tells me, "It feels like you're somewhere else."

I am.

In those moments, I'm with you.

Guilty as charged,
Red

9 1.

Beatnik said to her,
"I want to be
the best you ever had,"
from between her legs,

and she laughed.

She didn't know why
she laughed,
but she laughed
and the echo filled her throat,
swelling insufferably as it
extended to the depths of her belly
in shame and guilt.

He said,
"That's not possible is it?"

Her silence spoke for
itself.

"Oh god, it's not."
He said.

And she knew as well,
that it wasn't.
It never would be.

In any sense
of "ever had".

9 2.

But she never had Danger,
really,
did she?

That was how
they worked.

But he had her.
She knew then,
he had her.

Dear Danger,

I had another dream of you last night.

I was laying on a mattress that was signed by every woman you had ever kissed, and ever slept with, and ever shared with, and ever loved.

I don't even know the number, or if it was even close, but it was filled with stories about them and love notes all written for you.

And I slept on top of them to remind myself that you never belonged to me.

Realistically,
Red

9 3.

Even in Beatnik's presence,
his big, beautiful presence,
with his quirky printed boxers
he got from a monthly service,
and how he tried so hard
to cook for her
even though she wouldn't
ever eat,
and his unwavering love
for his mother,

she felt
so alone.

9 4.

After two weeks,
Danger came back
from New York.

TEN
BROKEN

9 5.

Danger began staying
at a friend's house
just across the street
from his parent's.

The walls were falling apart,
the light fixture in the bathroom
hung out of the wall,
the electrical needed rewiring,
the fence needed rebuilding,
and the dog mauled her
the first time she visited.

But all that mattered
was there was a mattress
on the floor
in one of the rooms,

and a place to lay
together
was all they ever
needed.

9 6.

She had to get used to
seeing Danger
again.

All while juggling
seeing someone else
who she didn't want to see
anymore
but didn't know
how to stop
seeing.

Every time she left,
she placed her heart
on his pillow
and felt its absence
in every day she spent
away.

9 7.

She felt guilty.
She felt guilty often.

She was the one
who pursued Beatnik
to finally have a relationship
with her.
She couldn't pinpoint why
anymore.

She wanted to know
if she was fooling herself,
if she wanted some
real stability.

But he bored her,
and he was not
boring.

But he bored her
all the same.

98.

Her phone service didn't work
at Beatnik's and she felt
anxiety in every moment
wondering if Danger
was trying to get a hold of her.

But she would agree
that he had that
hold
on her
without trying.

9 9.

Beatnik was not unintelligent.
He read her writing,
he knew not a word
was for him.
He knew her words
were all for Danger.

He knew she was withdrawn,
the way she wouldn't look him
in the eye.

And after two months,
he said,
"I don't want to be a safe bet.
I want to excite you.
I want you,
but you don't want me.
And that's okay."

So, while he was out hiking
the mountains,
they chose to not see each other
on his return.

Dear Danger,

You have broken me so delicately, silently, and effortlessly.

One day I realized I can't feel anything for anyone but you.

Hopelessly,
Red

ELEVEN
MATCHING
DARKNESS

1 0 0.

As a lovesick child
she believed souls consisted as one
in the galaxy,
and they wandered this existence
until they found their pieces
that had broken off in the chaos
of becoming human.

Time,
and mostly men,
made her doubt.

Then, she realized she felt an
unexplainable
reason to give him
every molecule she could exhaust
from her earthly vessel
that contained her.
To take nothing from his.
To love him
without conditions.

She believed once more,
but she was still
whole
alone.

She loved him madly,
but she was not mad
without him.

1 0 1.

But she did feel dreadfully mad
most days:

mad to live,
and mad to love,
and mad to be
more.

Madly,
madly,
more.

1 0 2.

He told her,
"Everyone's stress settles
somewhere."
In their muscles,
in their bones.
His stress was perched
comfortably
inside his back.
Her hands did their best
 at unsettling it,
breaking it apart.
As long as her fingers had feeling
they would work it out,
letting his skin breathe
without it
for a moment.

1 0 3.

He was always
on the move,
on the run.

He went back to Los Angeles
for a few days.

He told her,
"I wish I could pack you
in my bag.
fold you up,
tuck you away,
keep you with me
everywhere I go."

She told him
that he should.

Be he said
he wouldn't feel right
taking her along
in his nomadic life.

But what he didn't know
is that her heart:
she was a gypsy.

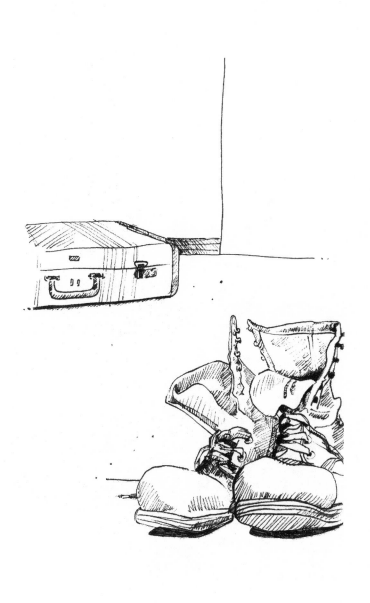

Dear Danger,

I lied, my dear, I lied. I do still cry. Maybe sometimes, only sometimes, it's not enough. Sometimes I want more. I want more from you. I would never ask you for more, but I wish you wanted more as well. I would treat you well, so well. I would treat you well.

Oh well,
Red

1 0 4.

She had a friend
who thought Danger
was a figment
of her imagination,
and she couldn't blame him.

He only came around
when he wanted to
and no one else saw him
but her.
His character was perfect
in her speech –
her mouth uttered only
flawless positivities.
She had uncaptured memories,
known only to them,
and not a single photograph
to prove
that they transpired certainly.
and she kept repeating the line,

"I swear
the unicorn exists."

1 0 5.

She said,
"Most people are awful,
you have to hold onto the ones
who aren't."

He said,
"No, all people are awful.
You have to hold onto the ones
whose darkness
matches your own."

Dear Danger,

I always over-think moments. Even while they're happening, I'm thinking about how I dream of those moments every moment we aren't together.

I'm thinking about how I'm taking them for granted and I want to do them over again, better.

Genuinely,
Red

1 0 6.

She had this,
what some people consider
bad, habit
of staring.
Where most would feel
uncomfortable with her
idle pauses, stark silences,
unapologetic, unbroken eye contact.
Small talk was useless
to her.
She could learn more
by submerging herself
in a gaze.
And until him,
everyone had looked away,
asked her what was wrong,
tried to fill the moment
with words.

He challenged her,
he stared longer, quietly
rooted himself inside her mind,
buried them in a sweet silence.
She felt safe in his eyes.
When he finally spoke
he asked
what she was smiling at.

She didn't even realize
she had been smiling.

1 0 7.

She was still seeing his quirks.

He made them
tuna sandwiches
and after they ate,
he tried to kiss her
while she ran around
the entire house
from him
until he caught her
with his tuna breath.

Or he would kiss her
like he was a rabbit
chewing at her
like she was his carrot.

In those endearing instances
she would say things like,
"You're so weird."
but really she locked it away
to reminisce about later.

She memorized those things,
She memorized
the silly moments,
he wouldn't think
she noticed happened
at all.

You are somewhere I feel
free,
stripped bare
you can see
down to my bones
that bend and break
in vulnerability
under your weight.
You are somewhere I feel
me.

Dear Danger,

Loves before you, I had wondered what they did for me, how they could help me, what they added to my life, how they progressed me, positively. I don't want men to save me anymore. I don't want someone to alter, modify, or repair me. I think the reason there were so many men in my past that would, is because I was subconsciously willing them to. When I loved – or what I perceived at the time as loving – them, I would only love them for what they did for me, how they could make me feel, what they could do for me.

As woman we are pushed in two directions. Either to be fierce and need no one, or to be subservient and let a man be half, or whole, of our beings. Most teeter somewhere in be-tween those two extremes, but I take from both. I am ravenous, but not selfish.

You do not complete me, but I've come to realize that no matter how hard I fight it, you have become a part of me. A part I didn't want, a part I didn't ask for. Nevertheless, a part that if it left me now, I would be lesser than I was before.

Lovingly,
Red

1 0 8.

He said,
"People are all
so easy to read."

She said,
"I don't understand them
at all."

He said,
"No, you do understand them.
You just don't understand why
you're not like them."

1 0 9.

She said, "I just need
reassurance sometimes."

He said, "With what?"

She said, "That I'm important
to you.
That you actively
want me in your life
and not by convenience
or circumstance,
but because you enjoy
being with me.

Because if that ever changes,
you can move on,
and I'll be hurt
but I always want to be
something positive
and someone you love
being around.

You are so good
at telling me that
I'm a wonderful person,
but I want to know
that I'm wonderful
for your life
as well.

I wouldn't want to be in it otherwise."

He said, "You are important
to me
and I want you
in my life."

And that
was enough.

TWELVE
MINE

Dear Danger,

I had a dream that we were lost in a universe composed of black and white.

I searched for you all night.

When I found you I said, "You look so different." And you said, "You do too." I kissed you and said, "Let's shed our skin, be alive again."

So, we painted our bodies and lived in color in the world of black and white.

My dear Danger, lets always live and love in colors others only dream of.

In screaming color,
Red

Dear Danger,

I'm no longer impulsive and sporadic. I don't implode at every moment. I am, dare I say, patient. I still need the rolling boil, but maybe I can simmer after all. Because, I have learned: the boil breaks the chemicals apart. The simmer melds them together. So, I'll simmer.

It isn't easy, my dear Danger, but I'll simmer.

Genuinely,
Red

1 1 0.

The third time
they drove to Austin
was a quick trip.
On the way back,
she drove
the last hour
and he fell asleep.
She kept looking over at him,
because it felt so nice
that someone
trusted her that much
to fall asleep
while she drove.

Something so,
seemingly, small,
yet, up until then,
no one had.

Dear Danger,

My thoughts are in disagreement, emotionally disharmonious.

It's as if you molded me, my original materials and body parts, my skin and bones, my blood, and my beating heart, my being, all of me.

And I felt every ridge in your fingertips – tender at times – smooth my cracks, repair my broken edges. Your steady hands – coarse at others – casted me unbreakable.

Then you put me back on the shelf and told me I could shine all by myself.

Yet, we didn't anticipate the retained tactile memory. My pieces and parts, bit by bit, every inch, long to be needed by you.

Genuinely,
Red

1 1 1.

She fell ill
and he came
to her aid.

Before,
men would assume
providing the tangible,
the material,
that no more effort
was needed.

A roof, money, security,
no compassion, or relief.

He didn't have
things
to offer,
but what he did have
he gave to her.

He gave her
comfort.

1 1 2.

Sometimes his inquisitions
felt more like interrogations,
but it wasn't his voice
she was hearing,
it was her
vulnerability
and her need to appear mysterious
and disarming
and to bewitch him
as he had her.

But when she thought about it
too much,
she felt like
nothing she said
made her seem
like she was
worthy
of his time,

so she said nothing
and then
she wasn't.

Dear Danger,

I'm insecure, and terrified.

That's why I act like I can't make a decision to save my life. I spent years surrounded by people who treated me like I was damaged, and I felt as if I was. Then I met you and you treated me like a human rather than a delicate, fragile glass that can shatter (and that had). But I still sometimes feel damaged. And because of that, I have so much fear, so much fear, of losing you. And because of that, I'm stupid. I lose myself around you, because I'm so scared.

I'm stupid, and I'm sorry.
I'm insecure, and terrified,
Red

1 1 3.

She was the girl who
could not be contained.
She was out of control.
But then,
she restrained
herself
for him.
She sheltered him,
from her.

On the inside,
in her mind,
she was still wild,
but in reality
she was confined,
to keep them safe.

And,
if it were up to her,
he would
never know.

1 1 4.

Then,
he fell ill soon after
she had.
She got to return his favor,
his care.
Her love for him
only reacted
in grandiose
reactions.

She got him two kinds of soup
in bread bowls
and dinner rolls,
because he liked those,
and medicine
and snuggles.

It was the first time
she spent the night
that they didn't make love,
but she rubbed his back
until he fell asleep
and she couldn't remember
a single time, in all their nights,
she went to bed
more satisfied.

1 1 5.

That night
he grabbed her
in her sleep
and pulled her close
and said something so quiet,
but she heard him.

"Mine."

She wasn't sure if he was
sleep talking
or aware,
but betwixt
wakeful and slumber
he said words
he wouldn't otherwise.

She had said,
she was only
sometimes
hers,

but wrapped up in him
she wanted nothing more
than to hear him utter
those words again,

"Mine."

Dear Danger,

I'm paying a debt I don't owe. For her mistakes, for your mistakes, for everyone who ever hurt you, for everyone you ever hurt.

I made my mistakes, but never with you. I hurt people, but never you.

You don't even know you're doing it, but I can not afford to pay any more.
I'm all out of change.

Defeated,
Red

1 1 6.

He told her,
"I don't deserve you."
and sometimes
he didn't,
but she wished
he did.

Dear Danger,

I'll always want what's best for you, even if it's not what's best for me.

I'm surrounded by a world that tells me, "Always put yourself first." But I'm too gentle, and too kind, and I love you far too much to ever care about myself.

They may think I'm weak, but I think simply loving someone without expecting them to love you in return, and willingly, and gladly, enduring all the circumstances that entails has made me, quite possibly, the strongest woman that I know.

Genuinely,
Lowe

THIRTEEN
WE WILL BE
OKAY

1 1 7.

Because of circumstances
unforeseen
for him,
and she was living
in a new place,
he started staying with her
for the first time
since they began
hanging out.
And she started finding his hairs
on her pillow,
and in her shower,
and in her sink,
and she had heard others
complain about
that very happening.
She couldn't say she understood,
because any piece of him
left behind
was a treasure, and
to her,
would always be
the sweetest thing.

1 1 8.

He told her,
"We are with each other
until if and when
we no longer want to be.
It's as simple as that."

And they were as simple
and as
complicated
as
that.

1 1 9.

She could feel his
remnants
within her,
stirring
every moment
that she was awake…
in her dreams…
or, veritably,
when she was breathing.

She could
see herself
growing,
rooting deeply,
inside of him.
Moving,
changing,
lasting.

And it was
serene.

1 2 0.

She tried him on,
a year prior.
He fit her
flawlessly.

She looked at photographs
from before then – a
vacant,
and empty,
cold
expression.
Same woman,
but she didn't
recognize herself.

She looked at her reflection
presently –
a glow,
radiating
poise
and self-sufficiency.
She knew her.

She believed
that love looked good
on her.

1 2 1.

He said, "let's make love
and take a bath."
So, they did.
They finished together,
her on him, him inside of her.
Candles and wine
and Otis Redding.
They soaked
and washed each other
of all the stress
that was in the world.
He kissed her bubbles,
while she massaged his.
They talked all night.

The next morning,
she lay in only his jean jacket
that he left her,
remembering a night
of being touched by him
inside and out.

Dear Danger,

Do you ever have movie-like sequences in your head that break off of reality? Like in Six Feet Under? Where you see something else happening entirely and then snap back into reality?

A song plays and you imagine yourself dancing together in a bare living room with only the essentials to survive and yet the room is so full because every inch is occupied with love?

Then it's back to waking live and all the moments that create friction and all the obstacles that make that break seem so far away from being real?

*I sometimes prefer my insanity
to reality.*

*A basketcase,
Red*

122.

She just wanted him
to be happy,
genuinely.

Even if it wasn't
with her.

That didn't mean
she didn't wish it was
with her.

She just wanted him
to be happy,
genuinely.

Dear Danger,

Someone told me today, "Whoever you're writing about, I hope they know how special you are."

And I told them, "He tells me everyday."

Every day,
Red

Dear Danger,

Most humans are vampires or viruses. They either latch onto others and thrive solely on the resources they obtain or they invade and grow exponentially while simultaneously weakening their host and taking over completely.

I am here to be neither.

I am here to be your refuge, to feed and supply. I am here to be your remedy, to nurture and alleviate.

I am here to transfer all my love to all of you until it's seeping out of your pores.

And you, you are my saboteur. You sabotage my fears and the anxieties that threaten me. You sabotage the parasitic and the empty, until I am left with wholly me.

Genuinely,
Red

1 2 3.

He held her hand in such a way
that she could feel their heartbeats
pulsing through their fingertips.

She never felt
so connected to humanity
or so alive
than she did while feeling
their very own blood
working so hard
to break through barriers
of vein and skin
to beat and pulse and
be
together.

1 2 4.

She laid in the bath
and used the soap
she bought for him
to use when he was
at her apartment.

It wasn't the same as
his scent
but it smells like
all the time they spent
in that tub
surrounded by
water and bubbles
and love.

1 2 5.

He said,
"No matter what happens,
we will be okay.
You and me."

He said, "If it's not,
then we can run away.
Put in our papers to
move to Canada."

She really wished
they could.

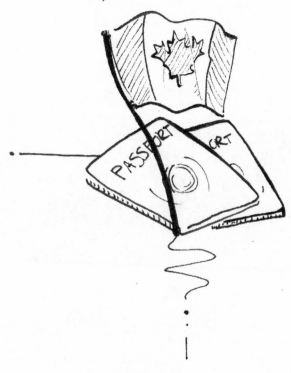

Dear Danger,

I have to remind myself daily: I commit myself to you completely, you have my heart entirely, but you never asked me for that. It has been my own doing.

I can't expect the same from you.

And I won't,
Red

1 2 6.

She did not need to ask,
and she did not need to know,
and she did not need to contemplate on
who,
or what,
or when.

The answers did not change
the time they spent together,
so knowing at all
never meant anything
to her.

She was happy
with her rule
"Don't ask, don't tell."

I miss you most
as you're kissing me goodbye.

1 2 7.

In the most
carnal and ravenous
of moments,
their eyes locked
with a power
and intensity
that jolted
a quiver
from their eyes
down her back
into the soles of her feet.

In that moment,
where he took her
and she took him,
equally and fully,
she saw that he was smiling
in his eyes
and his mouth
and inside
of her.

1 2 8.

She told him,
"no one has ever been
very good to me."

But that was not true.
There were people
who were good to her,
but she wasn't
very good to them.

He was the first time
she wanted to be good
for him
and not
for her.

Who I'm with
is not
who I am.

1 2 9.

She saw him
so much more
complex
than they did.

She didn't look to him
only to see
what he could
give to her.

1 3 0.

She always used to say,
"You never love again
like before you were hurt.
You never love again
like your first love,
before you had
your heart broken."

When she first met him,
she was selfishly loving someone
she thought was her first love.
He broke her
in every way you could
break someone.

Until they met again,
over a decade later,
she had never loved again,
though she tried,
and she failed,
and she tried,
and broke herself
more than anyone ever broken her,
so that she could put herself back together
on her own.

By the time he came back around,
she was prepared
to never love the same way
that she had before,

She was prepared
to love him better.

FOURTEEN
TASTE THE
BELIEF

1 3 1.

Her love for him
was her possession.

He was not,

but her love for him
was hers.

It was
so important
to remember that.

Dear Danger,

I used to buy into this entire concept that writers and artists are tortured and sad. That they self-medicate and are essentially big insecure piles of shit. That's true for some. I assume, most. But not for me.

In order to stop feeling so slighted by love, we all need to stop assuming that we deserve it.

No human being owes us anything, least of all their love.

Tortured is just another way to say selfish.

Not tortured,
Red

1 3 2.

His arm around her waist;
his mumbled gibberish;
a few snores, raspy breaths;
pretzeled legs;
his unconscious grabs,
pulling at her bare skin
in the dark,
begging without words
that she be
closer, closer,
closer still;
soft shoulder
and collar bone
kisses;
consistently rising body heat;
her ever quick heartbeat,
slowing, slowing,
slowing still;
not wanting to leave
the tender moment
where he has drifted off
and she held on
before slipping into
a blissful slumber;

whispering, whispering ,
with her fingers in his hair
things they won't remember
in the morning.

1 3 3.

In his absence,
her heart
did not grown fonder.

Her heart grew fonder
when it was against
his skin.
Her heart grew fonder
when she witnessed
the entire universe
nestled within him
through his eyes
as they were looking
into hers.
Her heart grew fonder
and fonder
and fonder
and her happiness existed
in every single moment
they were together.

In his absence
her heart
did not grown fonder,
but it did grow fonder
of the thought
of when it would grow fonder
in his presence.

Dear Danger,

The crisp air takes me to this time last year, where we spent most days with only each other's skin to keep warm. It was so much simpler then. It was pure, maybe naive, but I think every time it gets cold, for the rest of my life, in every winter, in every shiver, I'll remember sleeping on floors in sleeping bags and surviving on the flames of the raging fire of only our love.

Genuinely,
Red

1 3 4.

Seeing him dance,
and fly, and dream –
upon the stage, upon the screen –
living, loving; wild, free –
overflowed
and flooded her bloodstream,
got her heart rate escalating.

She said,
"Kiss me, kiss me.
Taste all the belief,
the belief I have in you
and how this is only
the beginning."

(Her drug was his success.)

Dear Danger,

My memory is not what it used to be. I used to remember everything, but now it's selective in its choosing. Too many people, places, things. I've lived so many lives, that my soul has aged further than my years. My memory is not what it used to be. I get mixed up, jumbled, I can't make sense of it, except when it comes to you. As if my brain and heart decided it only had room for you. I remember every word you ever said to me, and every place we've ever been, and all the dates of all the times we ever made love, but somehow I can't remember much of anything else.

My memory is not what it used to be. I still remember everything, but now everything is only you.

Genuinely,
Red

1 3 5.

She dreamed
of a different life
for them,
but she didn't want to
ruin the one they had.

So, she decided
to just live
them both.

She led
a double life,
but they were both
with him.

Dear Danger,

What I love about you, is that you're strong, and not the kind of strong that makes people sad: the kind of strong that suffers.

That's what I am. The kind of strong that has had to fight all their lives and the strength was necessary.

You're the kind of strong that seems like it was never weak to begin with: the kind of strong that remains when everything else

breaks.

Genuinely,
Red

FIFTEEN
VEGAS

1 3 6.

They huddled close together
under his coat
shuffling their belongings
from gate to gate.
Their early morning flight
canceled,
forcing standby status.

They began joking with her family
while suffering
their airport food of choice
about how he liked Topo Chico
more than her,
Her dad asked him
if there was a definitive list,
where did she rank
on this list.

He said the Godfather Trilogy
beats her.

He laughed,
and she pretended to.

She said that he's
not even on her list,
and he laughed
and she pretended to.

She know they were joking,

and she was too busy drinking
her overpriced coffee to follow up,
but he was on her list.

He was on the list, because
he was the list.

1 3 7.

While the stewardess
and pilot
were explaining
all the ways
things could go wrong,
by land, by sea,
she squeezed his hand
that was clutched
onto her leg
and just thought
that it would be okay
with his wings on her,
by land, by sea,
the things that could
go wrong
don't matter to the ones
that have gone right.

I would survive
without you
but I don't want to
have to.

I would survive
without you
but I would not live.

Dear Danger,

I never understood the thought, "If anything happens to me, I want you to know that I love you."

I do love you, but I don't have to say that for me or for you, because if I've loved you like I hope I have then you already know that.

So, dear Danger, instead I'll say, "if anything happens to me, I want you to know that you need to keep loving you."

Genuinely,
Red

1 3 8.

The glow around her fingers
outlined the mountains
created by the frigid air outside
meeting the glass separating
the heat rising inside
the room, their bodies
overlooking the sunset
while she screamed his name
to the entirety
of downtown Las Vegas.

Dear Danger,

Most people have no intention of knowing or seeing, so it still surprises me when I seemingly put up the same wall I do for them, for you. Yet to them it is concrete and to you it is glass.

Then you break right through,
Red

1 3 9.

He crawled into the hotel bed
next to her
and said, "I'm just waiting
for you to get bored
with me."

She laughed, properly
out loud.
"Amusing." She thought
to herself,
"he has no idea
that he's the only thing
that has ever made me feel
anything
at all."

I forgot to enjoy the memory,
while it was still
a moment.

1 4 0.

His fingertips brushed
where the dark circles
under her tired eyes
met her cheekbones
and presented her
with an eyelash.
This happened
what she thought was
three times
but what he insisted
was four.
She blew,
not gently
but with purpose.
She blew
her wish
into his fingertip.
She wished
(and wished
and wished
and wished)
the same wish.
The same wish she wished everyday,
but couldn't tell him.
She couldn't tell him
or it wouldn't come true.

"That's what they tell me," She said,
"but I think they're full of shit."

Dear Danger,

We agreed to never have any expectations of each other. Expectations only lead to disappointment. No desire, no suffering. I can only expect myself to fulfill my own self.

But I do expect, my dear Danger, that after loving you I'll never be the same.

Never,
Red

You can not find
your reflection
in other people
when it is
only found
in a mirror.

.

1 4 1.

She was not impressed
by the lights, the flash
by the sounds,
the ringing of the slots,
by the feel of the chips
she shuffled through her fingers
at a table
playing blackjack
with her sister.
She was not impressed
in a stool
drinking free booze
hitting a button
over and over
waiting for the right numbers
and symbols to line up.

She was impressed
by him,
the way he asked her dad
for help with his hands
in poker,
the way his eyes
and his voice
changed
when he got excited
for once.

She leaned over
and pressed her lips
up to his ear
and said, "I'm so glad
that you're here."
but, truth be told,
she was glad she was there

to witness
not the lights,
or the sounds,
or the booze,
but to witness

him.

The choices
you or I
make
are not validated
by others.

No one
has to understand
your choices
but
you.

Dear Danger,

I find myself trying to outrun our time together.
Like I am losing it before it is even over and I'm
hoping to trick it into not ever ending at all.

I'm still working on it,
Red

1 4 2.

His hand on her back,
firm and reassuring,
guiding her,
she had drank a few
by then.
Her feet stumbled
at times
but he smiled at her
and they were found
again.
She was found again
in his arms
on Fremont.
All he wanted
when they visited Las Vegas
was to see an Elvis impersonator,
so there they were,
outside in the cold,
two stepping
to a man in a white suit
who had thighs as big
as both of their waists
combined.
He was singing
the Frank Sinatra cover
of My Way.
His cheek on hers
his voice in her ear,
firm and reassuring.

She was counting out loud
instinctively,
and he told her to
just dance.
He spun her out,
turned her around,
pulled her back
a few times.
She felt restricted
by their coats
and her purse
over her shoulder,
but he dipped her
once
and he kissed her
more than that
and she sang with him
and just danced
in his arms
on Fremont.

1 4 3.

Some of her clothes
still smelled like smoke
from him
and that smoking room
in the hotel
on the 20th floor
with a view,
but all she ever looked at
was him.
And she thought
that he was quite
like cigarettes:
he was addicting,
and he was calming
and he felt
so nice.

And he lingered
with her
long after
he was gone.

SIXTEEN
A NEW YEAR

Dear Danger,

Kissing you in my kitchen at midnight while you played auld lang syne on your phone bookended my year. Kissing you from one year to the next. You have become my favorite tradition.

Auld lang syne, my love.
Red

Dear Danger,

On nights when missing you is unbearable, the things I think about are not always all-encompassing, flaming passion moments. We have those. We have plenty of those. But the nights I miss you most I think of your cigarette burning low between your fingertips, you leaning against the banister outside on my front porch, me standing on the other side of the door in lingerie, talking to you about so much and so little all at the same time, headlights passing by but no care — no care in the world — except your eyes burning low into me, holding a glass of champagne between my fingertips. Those times are just as cherished for remembering as the all-encompassing, flaming passion moments. The quiet glimpses of domesticity.

And home.

Genuinely,
Red

I think every time it gets cold
for the rest of my life
in every winter, in every shiver
I'll remember sleeping on floors
in sleeping bags
and surviving on the flames
of the raging fire
of only our love.

1 4 4.

She was out at a smoky jukebox dive
with one of her best friends.
The warnings on the television
told them a tornado was blowing in.
They could hardly see
out the glass doors
to the smoking patio,
and there they watched the storm.

An arm wrapped
around her neck
and a stark chill shot up
the spine of her back
before she soon recognized
his smell
and saw
his face
and discovered that
the weather on the roads
had brought him to her.

"Of all the gin joints
in all the world."

In the reckless abandon
of an unheeding storm,
they drank whiskey
and two-stepped
to old country songs.

Amarillo By Morning.

And when the storm died down
they created their own outside
in his car.
Fog on his windows
thunder in their bones
and their skin, it rained
it rained
it rained love
in a way
that little Texas town
won't soon forget.

1 4 5.

She was mounted astride him
in the driver's seat of her parked car
on a dark residential road
with a single dim street light.
He was still inside of her.
She was leaning up against
the steering wheel,
consciously avoiding
honking the horn.
They accidentally left
the headlights on,
so, they weren't as discreet
as they were hoping.
They were managing obstacles
with their living situations
and distressing over plans and means.

She looked at him,
"It's okay, we've been through worse.
You left me."

"Had to roll the dice,"
He said.

She smiled.
"I know."

"But I came back to you."

"Yes. You did come back."

He repeated,
"I came back to you."

She did remember the months
he was gone.
She would write almost every day,
"some nights are harder than others."
Looking back, she saw that
she missed him most nights.
In fact, she didn't stop.
It was a constant stream
that she attempted to dam up
and forget about
until the missing him broke through
every crack.

But yes.
he came back to her.

1 4 6.

Her favorite part
of dancing with him
was when the music slowed
and he pulled her closer to him
and his face was on hers
and she could smell his hair
and he kept singing to her
like she was the only other one
in the bar.

And in that moment
she felt like she was.

Dear Danger,

When I listen to that song and I hear that key change, I see you just as vividly as that night you danced with me. And I can hear your voice singing to me in that smile. I reached up to touch your face, reminding myself that you're real. And it's all in slow motion, like I'm watching a movie in my mind. On repeat. And sometimes I can't believe you ever happened to me.

Genuinely,
Red

1 4 7.

She was so easily changed
for the better
(growing, overflowing)
by him, with him,
because everything
he taught her
she felt like
she already knew.

Dear Danger,

Our visceral longing in physical absence manifests as ravenous desire, the sole need in our unconventional understanding, and the intangible yet fanciful speech exchanged fails to fill the void satisfied by only the phys-ical you.

To compensate, we spend days on end just making up for time and love lost.

But when we play house for just a few days, then we go back to our lives, it feels a lot like being a book on a shelf in an old neglected library that's been locked away for centuries and finally being discovered, and dusted off, and read unapologetically, and dogeared and highlighted, and creased and cracked, and loved so well, more than once, with all your favorite parts memorized and maybe a few written up on your notepad in your scribbled handwriting,

and then being put back.

I wish we could stay forever,
Red

And I'll never understand
how something that has elicited
superhuman strength from me
can be my greatest weakness.

Dear Danger,

Do you suppose we relive things and aren't even aware of it? Do you think there's other timelines, either before now or in conjunction with it, on other planes? These are the things I wonder about during my long busy, big city work commute, driving home and wondering how many times and in how many different lives I've loved you.

I imagine in all of them,
Red

1 4 8.

She said,
"Vulnerability
is a rarity,

but it's undeniably sexy
if it's granted.
The gestures, the instances,
that scare us a little,
that take us right to that edge
of feeling slightly uncomfortable,
are the ones that are unrivaled
and life,
and love,
changing."

There were such deeply
personal exchanges
that feel so natural
between that
that she forget how intensely intimate
that they were
until she thought on them later,
after he was gone,
when she was alone
and reliving him.

He crossed a threshold
she had never let anyone
beyond before

as if she let him into her
realm of being
that surrounded her.
And he did it in a way
that made it feel natural,
like he belonged there,
there inside her,
all along.

She said again,
"Vulnerability
is a rarity.

It's laying down
bare
wide open,
like a living cadaver,
and asking you
to dissect me.
Remove my heart,
keep it as your own,
and sew me up
when you are done.

Take it,
it's yours."

She finished,
"Vulnerability
is a rarity
but so am I."

SEVENTEEN
SOUL LOVE

1 4 9.

She, the key.
He, the deadbolt.
Shut up tight
until he entered her
where only he fit into.
He twisted and turned inside her,
moved, and changed
her design,
She opened up
as their earthly existence
melted
like they were merely
made of wax
rather than steel.

They unlocked a world
that was shut away
and there
they were
more than human.
Their bodies
did not contain them,
their souls could touch
and dance
and run,
and they did.

Only they could access
this plane
as it existed only within them

when their whole selves
melt
and meld
and they transferred
universes
there.

And each time
they came back
slightly different
than before.
As if she retained
pieces of him
and he retained
pieces of her.

They could hear things there.
Their words
did not restrict them.
Sounds were
more than language.
They could experience
emotions transferred
from one to the other,
with nothing lost
in translation.

They discovered there
all the senses,
and colors,

and beauty,
oh, the beauty,
that hadn't been
realized yet
by humanity.

She felt him there
all around her,
all within her,
like he was meant
to be felt
like only she could
feel him.
And she could feel him
feeling her
completely.
It was like an eternal,
continuous,
orgasmic experience.

Their souls
could make love,
and they did.

Dear Danger,

I never believed in "my other half", because I'm a complete earthly vessel, but I have come to know that we share a soul.

I do feel your absence viscerally. So much, in fact, that sometimes my heart feels more broken than it's ever been. Even though it's more whole than it's ever been.

The space mimics a blinking bulb flashing on when you are with me and switching off when you're away, needing your light inside me all the time and growing tired of, and nigh fearful of, the flicker.

Genuinely,
Red

Dear Danger,

I can't wrap my head around most societal norms and concepts. I don't understand humans. I don't understand relationships. I don't think I'll ever shake how different I feel. How when I love you, I don't want to owe you or own you, how I don't want to be owed or owned by you either. Sadness and betrayal comes from feeling like you deserve to receive something from someone else, that it is only in their own capacity and power to give. You don't deserve anything from anyone but yourself. Humans are all separate beings. I burn up in love, but I belong to myself as much as you belong your yourself. I am at war every day with this, because I hear the words from everyone else. All I see around me are expectations. Expectations from others. And most only giving to get some-thing in return, even subconsciously. That's what the very premise of a relationship is: expectations, sacrifices, compromises. That's fine, but it doesn't feel natural to me. I don't understand the human existence. I believe we are all free. Free to live. Free to love. And there is no pain when you ask for nothing.

Genuinely,
Red

1 5 0.

Romance to her
didn't sound like
flowers, and apologies,
diamonds, and lies,
material things
that would never
satisfy her.
Transient paled to
their transcendence

No, it sounded like,
"I just want
a small place
I can afford

and you
sharing the
sleeping bag."

1 5 1.

She had inescapable daymares,
terrors in full consciousness,
of him falling in love
with another face, another body,
another soul
that wasn't hers.

She knew she was not
inordinately extraordinary
in any way.
Just a face, a body, a soul that once
broke away from his.

So, why wouldn't he?
So, why couldn't he?
He can, he may
and she would let him.

Because her face, her body, her soul
loved his,
and, though she was not, her love was
inordinately extraordinary

and even if they weren't,
it would be
quite indefinite.

Dear Danger,

*Your jean jacket is still hanging on the chair at my desk
in my room. When I glance too quickly, I think that it's
you.*

*I put it on and lay naked in it awhile, just to smell you
and feel it on my skin.*

*My soul, I usually lock her in this box, this tiny box
in me I keep hidden away in the darkest corner, where
no one can find her.*

*And it's quiet there.
And she doesn't miss you so much.*

*I'll give her your jacket
just in case she gets cold.*

*Genuinely,
Red*

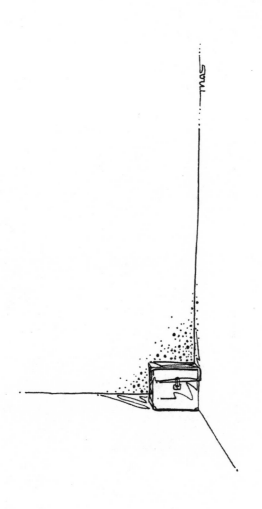

TIFFANY LOWE

Dear Danger,

I was going through my notes and one from the other night before you showed up simply reads: "You." And sometimes I feel that's all that needs to be said.

But speaking of words, fine fine words: whoever knew that the finest words you would ever speak to me would be four instead of three:

"You're my best friend."

As you are mine,
Red

Dear Danger,

*I do not care what anyone thinks of us. Or our
unconventional lives.*

*Let them talk, and talk, and talk. I can't hear them over
the sound of the difference of who we are. It changes
nothing, we'll drown them out. And turn their wails into a
chant. a battle cry. And instead of swords, we'll use
our lips, and make love instead of war.*

Genuinely,
Red

1 5 2.

She had this way
of following up
the scarce, delicate statements
(where she stripped the layers
and could actually feel the words
on her skin)
with illuminated remarks,
surely light enough
to float the substantial load
(it's aplenty, but it's fragile)
a few inches where
it idled in mid-air,
just far enough away
to where she didn't have
to claim it.

And she laughed.

Dear Danger,

I fight this urge often, more often than I can even count, even admit, to call you up out of the blue just to say, "I love you."

Those words come out of my mouth subconsciously, inadvertently, every time I think of you. But I believe it would be for no one's benefit but my own and I promised myself that I would nev-er let this become

that.

And I get these similar urges to call you and just say, "Can I drive to your side of town? I just need to feel you and then I'll leave. I am not asking much, just for you to touch me. When you feel me, I feel myself again. I just need to feel you and then I'll leave."

I hold the phone in my hand and I don't dial. Either time. And it gets difficult to breathe, so difficult.

But I keep breathing and I keep being just fine.

Just fine.

Love,
Red

EIGHTEEN
YOU WERE EVERYTHING

Dear Danger,

I wish you could borrow my eyes the way you've borrowed my heart and pieces of my soul, so you could wear them like glasses for a day. To look in the mirror and see what I do when I look at you. Words are just words. You'll never believe me until you can see it, too.

I'm so sick of words — empty, empty words — and yet, it's all I have.

I wish I had more,
Red

1 5 3.

It was 1:00am
and he had just traveled an hour,
after an extensive night
at rehearsals
and she was drifting off
on the couch
clad in a tiny, kinky outfit
she had assembled just for him.
She had work at 8:00am
and their opposite schedules
conflicted with normal patterns
of human sleep,
but she had waited up for him
patiently, impatiently
and when he arrived, his eyes
(god, those eyes)
scanned her so deliberately
and he paused with that half smirk
He told her she looked sexy
even though she knew
she looked tired
but, she thought
he looked sexy too, her Danger,
and she had been
waiting up all night.

And they burned
the whole place
down.

Dear Danger,

What happens in my day drifting, in my night wandering, in my outdated exhaustive index of fears and doubts that creep up behind me like a bullet to the back, that don't live under my bed, rather in my sheets, and in my head. What happens there is worse than anything you could do or say to me, because before you've ever spoken to me each day, my mind has run through all the possible scenarios. And it is not lost on me how unfair it is to you that I'm already prepared for all the pain you have yet to cause.

I'll work on it,
Red

Dear Danger,

One day I might look back and wonder what I was thinking. I want to tell her, future me: I was thinking of karaoke nights, dancing in jukebox dives, bird watching over that bank of trees and a dried up riverbank, bubble baths and candle light, playing dress up in fantasies, fogging windows in apartment parking lots and street corners with busted street lamps, last minute road trips for the day or for weeks at a time, hotel rooms with views of downtown — whatever city, it didn't matter, it never mattered — so many mornings talking politics and world views with coffee mugs and cigarettes, and sweet comfortable silences, and folding chairs on whatever patio — it didn't matter, it never mattered — boxsprings versus sleeping bags, on carpet versus tile floors, and wicker versus leather couches — it didn't matter, it never mattered.

There wasn't an us, but there was me, and there was you, and there was so much laughter, and so much love.

That's what I'll tell her, future me:
I was thinking … I'm sorry, I wasn't.
It didn't matter. It never mattered.

Love,
Red

Keep your emotions
in your control.
Do not repress them,
but do not let them
control you.
You are the machine,
they are just
the parts.
You decide,
you always decide,
which ones are working,
which need repair,
and which
need to be put away
for the long,
long winter.

Dear Danger,

Your walls surround not just you, they surround me too. Protecting me more than they are rejecting me. I have come to know that you, dear Danger, love me more while making me feel loved less.

And it only makes me love you more.

Genuinely,
Red

Dear Danger,

I want you and miss you all the time, but is that part of the allure? If I ever really had you as my own would I even want you anymore? If we ever had something traditional would you bore me to tears like every relationship eventually does? I can't answer that and maybe I'll never have to.

I'm not sure if I even want to know,
Red

(Spoiler:
It would bore her.

They found out much later,
that stability was not meant for them,
and she ripped it out
from under them again,
where they resumed their balance
harmoniously.

Their love was much like
a tightrope walker.
Delicate, and dangerous,
and they were in love
with life
on the wire.)

1 54.

They were
what was known as
"blue on black"
(blue ink would never
show up
when used atop
black.)

He coated her skin,
completely and intimately,
the shade of a raven's wings.

Distinctively onyx-tinted while
everyone else dripped cerulean
from their fingertips.
Deeming themselves irrelevant
to them
who hid, still intertwined,
in the dark spaces between
the light.

155.

Instead of providing shelter,
protecting her from harsh winds
where she would never learn how to
sustain them,
he stood out in the rain
with her
chilled right down to their bones
and he said,
"You are capable
of being anything
and, today, is a perfect day
to be
wet."

Dear Danger,

I remembered you, because I am still in love with you from when we were the same star. I can still feel you breaking away from me and floating in space beside me, aimlessly searching for home, when it is right here inside me.

You still consist of stars and I feel the gravity of every single one, pulling at me, and I feel the need to help them each shine like I know they are meant to.

You are a galaxy and you are infinite to me.

Genuinely,
Red

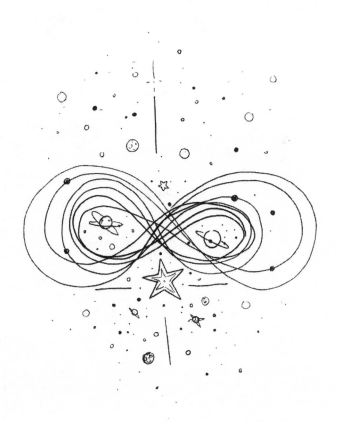

Thoughts do not,
and cannot,
define us,
nor do we have to attach to
– or identify with –
our thoughts.

Remember this
in every negative thought.
Do not give them
any of your energy;
they only possess the power
you give to them.

Be at peace today.

Dear Danger,

I think you believe I could be anyone if the same circumstances presented themselves, but I don't believe the same is true. I have been the worst in every relationship I've ever had. I've felt trapped and bored, but with you, I am perfect. You say I'm wonderful, but really, I'm wonderful for you.

If nothing else, I knew you. You might replace me one day with someone new, but you should know that, for me,

you were everything.

Genuinely,
Red

NINETEEN
MANHATTAN

1 5 6.

A picture perfect painting of them:
best seats in the house
in a quaint theater
on Broadway,
a show she had anticipated
all year,
a scene and song
that shattered her heart
right back into the pieces
that it used to be.
She stifled the sobs, but the tears
flowed steady streams
down both cheeks.
She shifted in her seat,
away from his sight line
to hide
from him
and the pain, discretely
(not so discretely)
and she felt his hand on her knee.
She glanced down to see
his handkerchief.

He saw her
even when she was hiding
but her let her be
as she would be,
separately.
He lent her his grace
and comfort, with ease.

He was there,
right there,
for her,
but he let her
be.

1 5 7.

Waking up every morning
next to him
on a fold out futon
padded by a mattress pad
with the sun coming through
the open window,
with the old rotting
wooden shutters
she had opened to have her coffee
and watch the hustle and bustle
and he took her
right there against the glass
where they all could see.
The lock fell off the door
and the shelf fell off the wall
and there might have
only been room enough
for two bodies
in that tiny studio apartment
off 75th in Upper West Side,
but that's all the room
they needed.

On their last night they drank
out on the stoop with friends
who came and went
as they pleased,
had a New York hot dog or two,
and she finished off
an entire bottle of wine

and stereotypically cried
about how much she loved him
as the rats scurried up and down
that old Manhattan street.

She didn't say it,
she never did.
She just wrote it
for the entire world to see.

She would keep writing it.
And thinking of little moments
like when he didn't say a word,
he just tucked her hair
behind her ear
and stuck a little earbud in,
and held her close,
and danced with her
while they waited for the subway.

For four short days (he was hers)
she was dreaming with him
and she would never forget that dream
of old Manhattan.

TWENTY
BLANK SLATE

1 5 8.

He was still inside her
and she could feel in her nerves
and in her veins
how tense she was,
clutching his neck for dear life
and there she was again –
a scared little girl,
begging, all but screaming,
to be saved.
His arms were draped
around her body
so lackadaisically
and it didn't feel constricting
or like she had imagined it should feel
when you are "saved."

He only held her tight enough
to know he was there,
rather than keeping her
for himself.

She could hear him telling her,
"You can save yourself."
and she did.

She melted.
She relaxed on top of him
and sighed in his arms.
And she saved herself.

Sometimes it takes
someone you love
more than yourself
to tell you
that you're not loving
yourself
enough.

Dear Danger,

Are you still content in blurred lines and structureless, wandering eyes? All for the sake of freedom and choice. Sacrificing loyalty from someone who loves you. Is that really free?

I managed to find the other half of my soul in a sea of transcendent lives, but I can't seem to find the rationalization of existence. I don't know how to reconcile it (existing) with the evidence that nothing matters (or lasts at all).

I feel tethered to nothing, to no one. Maybe at one point that felt freeing. Now it just feels lonely.

I'm sorry.
I'm still working it out,
Red

When coloring
outside of the lines
one may either drown in
overly blended pigments
or they learn
to embrace the
entire canvas
as a blank slate.

Sometimes
the epic love story
is only epic
to the one who wrote it.

Dear Danger,

Some of the hardest conversations I have are with myself.

I argue with my logic. I argue with my sanity. I argue what is right, what is wrong. Worse for the wear, because my own mind can't change my own mind. and it can't seem to make it up either.

And I always seem to wonder: when my heart's most private thoughts are turned into words on a page, is it even real?

Are we even real?
Or are we just a story now?

Does anyone know?
Red

1 5 9.

It was a lot easier
when she relied a lot less on
him
being around.

She was a lot less happy
but it was easier.

Dear Danger,

I don't feel attachment like others do. And I want to more than anything. With everything I should justifiably bleed for, but I don't. Other than my art. Nothing else makes me feel that way, like I want to pour myself into it completely.

Until you.

And it's effortless and instinctual. I don't expect that in return. I just expect you, whatever that is.

Just you,
Red

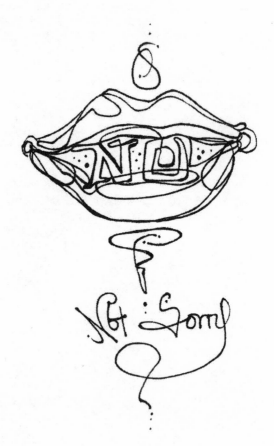

TWENTY ONE
FUCKBOY

160.

She was sitting there with him.

She called him Fuckboy,
and he would have resented that.
But at one point
he treated her
like she was disposable
and she tried
far too hard
not to be.

He was ten years her junior.
And they spent two months together,
before Danger came around.

They had a handful
of wild times,
where they were mostly high.

But then he left her,
back to college,
without even a goodbye,
but the tables turned.

She was the one
he couldn't get over.

And she,
well,
she called him Fuckboy.

1 6 1.

Now, was sitting there with him,
next to a fake crackling fire,
trying to drink enough
to forget about Danger,
the way she thought
he forgot about her.
She was telling stories –
she was always the storyteller –
and he remembered everything
she'd ever said to him,
and her favorite song,
but he didn't know her
at all.

And he was debating
if he would kiss her or not,
and she thought she had to prove
to herself
in some way,
by being there with him,
that she didn't want to kiss him back.

And she didn't.

She had always wondered,
the last few years,
if she saw him again
if she would eat her words –
the ones she told Danger
all the time –

that he was all she wanted
even if she could have
anyone in the whole world.

But she didn't eat her words.
She didn't even
let him
touch her.

She said no.
She said no and told him to leave.

Then he told her he
would
kiss her.
And he told her that she wanted to
and she turned away from him
more than once.

She thought,
"It's true, what they say,
if you don't want to kiss someone
you won't.
Things don't just happen
if you don't let them."

She told him she wasn't sorry
and she told him she didn't want to.

He said, "I know why.
You love someone
and all you want is him."

And after that
all his words faded out.

She had never told him that
and yet he knew it
and that's how she knew
that her words were not just words,
since she had never fed them to him
and there he was spitting them out.

She wanted to cross-stitch
the words
on the bed
they slept on:

"I love you
and only you.
I want you
and only you."

And, as she had told him,
it was not for lack of trying
now.
It was an inescapable
truth.

TWENTY TWO
THE CALM

.

1 6 2.

Pretty bird
in a big steel cage
with a creaky
wide open door –
a cage
she built herself.
A wild thing
who realized
she was perfectly happy
confined
where only he
could witness her.

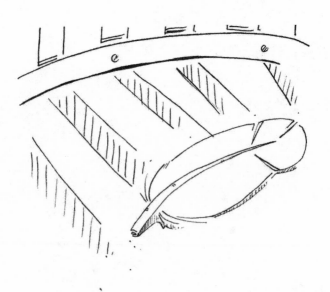

1 6 3.

Riding shotgun in his truck
with the windows down,
listening to him
sing a bluesy folk song,
cigarette hanging out the window,
and the wind blowing her hair
as she thought,
"I couldn't possibly
love anyone more."

164.

The view on her balcony
while she was standing inside,
clad in only a smile.
She saw him in between
each hanging blind
and the beams shining through
branches and branches
and birds jumping from limb to limb
and the back of his
raven-haired head
as he stared out
while the moon covered the sun
and the sky dimmed
only partly
but his radiance overcompensated
and she was too busy being blinded
by him
to be blinded by
the eclipse.

Dear Danger,

Remember watching the eclipse with me? Tonight the moon is waxing.

On the nights that the moon is crescent shaped like this I call it my Cheshire Cat moon. Like it's smiling at me. It's my favorite kind of moon. The nights I see it are always really significant to me. It's usually an omen that everything is going to be okay. I think that's true. And you're partly why. You said earlier, when you were inside me, that you like making me feel good. You do. In every possible way a human can make another feel good.

I think my Cheshire Cat moon is smiling for you tonight.

I know I am,
Red

1 6 5.

They told her for the longest time,
while he was tucked beneath
her sheets,
that he was a boogie man instead -
hiding underneath his bedframe.

They told her for the longest time
that she had simply painted him
on her life's canvas
with all her pretty watercolor words
but that he was actually
charcoal and lead.

They told her for the longest time
that he was a figment, or a mirage,
magic, or a fairytale -
a fictitious romantic fantasy.

She had tried to materialize him
at will, and he was steeped
in her every dream,
but he was more ghostly
than whimsical -
orbs in the moonlight
then up in smoke.

They told her for the longest time
to question everything,
but even if he was make believe
she would still believe in him.

Dear Danger,

I remember writing so long ago how what I felt for you was so selfless and pure and that is a love that is so hard to maintain.

I'm not always sure that I am strong enough to keep loving you so selflessly, but I will try.

I will try.
Until my last breath,
Red

Love
is such a heavy word that
I can't hold
unless you're supporting
the other side.

Our limbs are only meant
to wind
and intertwine
then keep growing
like vines.

Dear Danger,

I am genuinely happy. You are part of that. As we have evolved together I admit to feeling frustrating and obnoxious feelings. That I suppress, because it's not something I want anything to do with. I still only want your happiness. And that you choose to spend your time with me is, and always has been, enough for me. I'm never going to tell you who and what you can do. But, in the sake of honesty, because I have no idea if you're openly seeing other people, I often fill in my own thoughts. Which, admittedly, isn't healthy. I don't always grasp us as a concept. But we have never fit in a box and I've never wanted us to. I am very happy with that. If we did, I would be unhappy. I don't care about normal relationships. What we have is so much more than that. But because we have left so much open for interpretation I sometimes fill gaps myself. And it doesn't always end up being true. Then I get silly.

You are everything to me. How I treat you is not a way I've ever treated anyone. I only want to give you everything positive and loving that I possibly can.

Genuinely,
Red

1 6 6.

A love like the secret garden:
untouched, and pure,
yet managed not
nor maintained,
vines hidden away
to grow wildly.
Seasons elapsing
with leaves a-changing
and clouds passing,

She kept the garden to herself,
"It is mine, it is mine,"
she said, under her breath
as she unlocked the gate,
clutched the key
tight to her chest,
as she imagined another
roaming the garden paths
in her absence,
making no alterations to its beauty,
it still induced a silent sorrow
with the inability for her to accept.

She struggled with wanting
the whole world to see and
preserving a sweet sanctuary,
But for then,
she locked the gate behind her,

"It is mine."

Dear Danger,

I used to ache for you when it rained and now listening to makeshift raindrops on my pillow is the only way I can sleep alone.

And I dream of us making love in the rain every night.

Genuinely,
Red

1 6 7.

For her,
the storm came first.

Years of living in
a soggy cardboard box
out in a hurricane
before he showed up,
put a shiny coin
in her pruned, dirt-creviced hand,
a warm blanket around
her shaking shoulders,
kissed her chattering mouth
and told her
to dry her water-logged skin
to the bone:

the calm
had finally arrived.

TWENTY THREE
STILL

Dear Danger,

Your new apartment is Manhattan reminiscent and I think that's why my first footsteps inside were already familiar. A tiny creaky staircase and door handles that are barely hanging on their hinges, newspaper on all the windows, a tiny futon and a sleeping bag.

And you and me:
living artists.

My notebooks and paperbacks, my laptop and my book working. And you on the phone all day, between kisses and lovemaking, making things happen, making a movie, making me fall in love again and again.

And though I've lost everything, you've taken me in and let me share your space with you. And given me everything of yours to replace everything I've lost.

I can't thank you enough,
Red

1 6 8.

In her reflection one morning
she noticed her smudged fingerprints
blurring out the edges
of the outline of her face.
Mementos
left behind
from when they got home late
from a holiday party
the week before,
where he sang Great Balls Of Fire
(just like he had two years prior
in that little dive bar
strung up with Christmas lights).

He pulled her red, vintage,
high-waisted skirt
up over her hips
as soon as they walked inside,
pressed her up against the mirror
and took her like he had wanted to
all night.

She thought about wiping them off,
but decided to leave them.
She liked the reminder
that he still, two years later,
wanted her
that badly.

1 6 9.

They entered the limbo
that most teeter in
for only a moment
and they got lost there.

They took that uncertainty
that manifests as unrivaled passion
(and sometimes insanity)
and held it in stasis.

They found a way to live there:
in desire,
everlasting.

1 7 0.

She could set up camp
in the stubble of
his beard.
Each hair a tree
she'd hibernate
between
until his lips
woke her
in the spring.

Dear Danger,

You turned the girl who paints with the alphabet, who only had her words, into actions.

I was always "all talk", pretty words, never enough. But with you, I don't even need words. I'm all actions. All showing, no more telling. I don't have to say a thing that you don't already know. And, to me – the girl with all the words – for you to be the only one in the world to not need them from me, I think that says everything.

More than any label could,
Red

Fuck going easy on me
or letting me down gently.
Flames are not fragile
and he who holds me is the one
who should be cautious:

I will not be easy on him.

1 7 1.

A deep, dense fog pressed rudely
against their frosted window panes,
A cruel, cold draft slithers in slyly
like a snake with a harsh hiss
and a brutal bite.
Nature is sometimes sweet and supple
when it sprinkles a soft dew
that beads up on the blades of grass.
And it is sometimes so unkind,
like now,
with unforgiving, frigid hands.
His bare skin and the crook
right under his clavicle
where the side of her face fits
like a missing jigsaw piece
is a refuge, a cave she stowed away in
to hibernate in a relentless winter.
But he, her Danger, was
her favorite place to hide away
to rest her weary head
and calm her anxious heart
until the scent of his wildflowers
that bloomed from the crown
of his head
and curled over his brow
tenderly tickled her nose.
And his honeysuckle lips
pulled nectar from deep
within his roots
and invited her tongue

for a taste.
And the talking bird who lived
in the cage of his ribs
made her blood dance
with the sound
of its song.

1 7 2.
Instead of seeing
mountains
out of mole hills,
she saw grains of sand.

And living in an endless
paradise
was so much happier
than always
climbing.

1 7 3.

She said, "Don't you know
where my heart is
by now?"

He said, "In your chest."

He always reminded her
that her pieces
were her own.

And that's why
she let him
borrow them
(for a lifetime
or two.)

Dear Danger,

One of my favorite things about living with you is when you sing and you don't know, or don't care, that I'm listening. Whether it be in the shower or sitting in your little wooden chair with your guitar and harmonica. It entrances me just as it did all those years ago.

I've watched you sing, with that raw, bluesy voice, with a smile I can't seem to describe. It's a rare kind of smile that insists on happening. A kind of smile that you can feel in more than just your face.

I feel just like a fan, watching a man on a stage that she adores and admires, throwing her panties up on stage as she fantasizes over him touching her skin rather than just her underwear.

And then, each night when I press my bare body against yours, and I can't possibly mold myself into you any more, like when you mix the playdough colors, I hum a little tune to myself and that smile shares our sheets.

Your biggest fan,
Red

1 7 4.

One of her biggest fears
was that no one would ever be
what her dad was to her.
And what was even harder to deal with
was know that was one of her dad's
biggest fears as well.
She hoped, before he left her,
that she could show him that maybe,
just maybe,
she could be that for herself.

Two clouds of stardust particles,
puffs of smoke to the naked eye,
mingling, flirting with
the concept of merging.
Swirling about,
fragments of each
splintering off into the other.
Entangling and untwining
again and again.

Lovers
engaging in
the only dance
there is.

TWENTY FOUR
ALL MY LIVES

Dear Danger,

I used to think happiness might bore me. I wasn't sure, I only guessed because I felt trapped in traditional happiness that never made me happy in actuality. I got addicted to pain. I hurt myself to make sure I could feel alive. I thought high highs could only come with low lows. Until genuine happiness happened to me. Until you happened to me. I've never loved myself more. And now I'm sky high and never coming down.

Never,
Red

1 7 5.

There was a time when
there were questions,
an inquiring,
a back and forth
of learning each other.
That doesn't happen anymore.
She knew him.
They could comfortably exist
in silence,
which is what she always knew
love looked like.
But, admittedly, there is sharing
where he forgot to even breathe
because he had so much
to say.
He was a certain kind of beautiful
when he was vulnerable in words.
And all she could do was smile
and absorb him
all he want her to
until they rested
comfortably back into
what she always knew
love looked like.

Responsibility for your actions,
your feelings that stemmed
to the actions,
your situations that triggered
the feelings,
reside within you.

Dear Danger,

*If you're always giving all your words to those who
need more validation than any one human being could
ever give, at the end of the day there are no words left
for me. You say that it's just work, but you say your
work is your life.*

Which is it?

*I'm jealous of the women who share your art and craft
with you, because you'll never let me.*

*I have to watch from the sidelines and on specific
strategic days and times and within a parameter that
you're comfortable with. You keep me separate from your
work. I am elusive and illustrious, subtle and strong.
They don't see my face. They don't know my name.*

*But I pluck you from reality where the rest of existence
pauses. It doesn't exist. And I love you beyond
measure or limitations. They too do not exist. Only
you and only me. Only smiles and sighs.*

*You are my sanctuary, but I still want every part of you I
do not get.*

Slightly shamefully,
Red

1 7 6.

Every day
she was surrounded by bound pages
and pages
of stories
of varying topics
told by an eclectic
chorus of voices
on all spectrums.

She remembered a time
those she clutched in her hands
and held tight to her chest
were those of love.
Until romance felt cliche
and weak
and unimportant
in the grander scheme.
They didn't seem
big enough.

So all those stories
collected dust.

She had thumbed through
bound pages
and pages
and all the information
she had collected,
after all that time,
led her back to

believing in the magic
of the stories
that seemed
so small,
but contained
her entire heart.

She concluded,
"Love is all that matters
after all."

Dear Danger,

You have gone to bed with witches and are surprised that they have cursed the skin you sleep in. You might not have invited them to sleep in our bed, but our sheets can still sense them and so can I.

Who you're with when you're not with me and what you do with others does not affect what we have, unless it continually haunts and hurts us. Then it does. Please continue to think of me, even in passing.

This is not a threat, merely a request: please, do not take me for granted.

As you tell me: "make good choices."

I hope you make the right ones for us,
Red

Someone can love you
how they perceive
giving love looks
an amount they think
is extraordinary
and you still won't feel it
unless that's how you perceive
how receiving love feels.

1 7 7.

"Breathe,"
She told herself,
"just breathe."
Because what mattered was:
they shared a soul
and a life
and a bed.
And she knew his muscles
more intimately than her own.
She kneaded them well
and well and well
with loving hands
until they ached
down to the bones.

And she only asked of him
to keep her warm
with his precious vessel
of a body
that contained
all the pieces of her
that were his
to keep.

1 7 8.

He had her
since that first night
at the Landing,
when she showed up
and he was waiting for her
at the bar
and he looked back at her
with a smile
like Jack
at the top of the staircase
on the goddamn Titanic.

Like he had been waiting
all his life
and he had
so much to show her.

She took his hand
like Rose
and, oh,
how they danced.

If it's not this lifetime
that we are destined for
then it is another
and I'm sincerely
at peace
with that.

I will love you
for all my
lives.

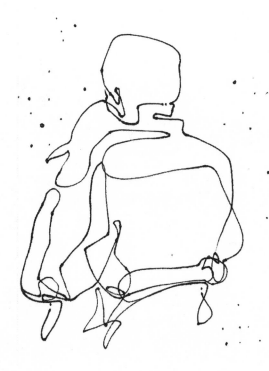

TWENTY FIVE
WHAT STORIES ARE MADE OF

Dear Danger,

I'm so glad that I don't need all the (constant) reassurance that every other woman in your life has needed.

After all, there's only so much you can give.

Give it to them. I don't need it.

Genuinely,
Red

1 7 9.

"Smile more.
Love him harder,
especially when
it's harder.
And never let a moment pass
where he would ever doubt
how infinite he is
to you."

She said to their mirror
every morning,
while the flames were still sleeping,
preparing herself to
remember to be grateful
for a raging fire
in a winter,
where most
just froze.

Dear Danger,

Some people get drunk and do rebellious and scandalous things.

I get drunk and the scandalous and rebellious thing I want to do is tell you that I love you.

Loving you in this world we live in is a rebellious act.

A rebel,
Red

1 8 0.

She was staring at him
while he driveled on to her.
She heard his words
but she was mostly thinking about
how she absolutely believed
they would write stories of him
one day,
of his conviction, of his craft.

And she could only hope
she would be
(a small part)
in them.

1 8 1.

Sometimes she thought of
the simplest of moments
that she missed:
like drinking black coffee
with him
on a balcony or porch
while he smoked a cigarette
or two.

He quit smoking,
and they didn't have
a balcony or porch
anymore,
and as she remembered it
so fondly –
their intimate conversations
over sips and drags –
what she found
most interesting of all:

She didn't even
like
black coffee.

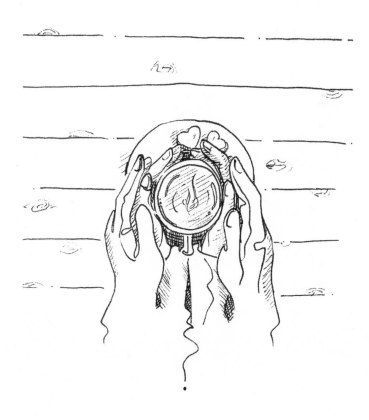

1 8 2.

They didn't have
a storybook,
romcom,
hit pop song,
kind of love.

They would never be
photobooth photos,
or proposals in the park.

It was more like
notebooks filled with verses,
letters scribbled on hotel paper,
four walls, floors, a roof, and skin,
kind of love.

You can either
see the obstacles
in the path
or you can envision
the way around them
(or over them
or under them.)
There's always a way around
(or over
or under.)
There's dead ends,
but there's got to be
that first time:
someone has to be
the one
to fork the road.
Look for a way around
(or over
or under)
or be the one.
Fork the road.

Dear Danger,

Last night I dreamed we never met, but I, and I alone, remembered everything from this life.

I tried to see you, but your eyes didn't seem to see me back the way they do here.

I sat mid-circle a crowd of people I didn't know as tears streamed down my face and I told them about you, about us: but there, it was only a story.

I was being surrounded by flowing curtains blowing around my naked body in a stark white room with bright, hot lights that blinded me and burned my skin, laying face down sobbing, alone.

I asked myself, between gasps of air, "Is this what dying is like?"

I know it was just a dream, but I believe it's the closest I've ever come. And now I know that dying must feel like looking to your eyes and them not looking back at me. I hope I never know that feeling in waking life unless I'm really gone.

Genuinely,
Red

1 8 3.

After a family event,
she thought about how
Beatnik would have fit in
seamlessly.

And, by then,
they might even be married.
He would have smiled fake
like they did
and pretended to care.
Or maybe he just might have.
He would have acted like it mattered
either way.

But Danger didn't know
how to do that.
He didn't know how
to be anything else,
but true.

And she was grateful to have that
versus the fake smiles, fake life,
any day.

No one owes you anything.
Nothing.
If you remember this,
everything they do
is either less painful
or more brilliant,
because they never owed you
anything.

TWENTY SIX
NOT SORRY
(OR SAD)

Isn't it interesting
the thoughts we project onto others
that we feel about ourselves?
Try to be aware
of the words and thoughts
you put into other's
mouths and minds
that are merely
a figment of your own.

TIFFANY LOWE

Dear Danger,

One of the hardest things to accept as a mere mortal is all the things you can't control. How I can't make you care any more than you choose to. How I can't make an impact deeper than you'll allow. How I could just disappear and you'll find someone else to fill my place yesterday.

But I will love us both enough for the both of us. If I expend the best of me on you, do not fret.

I want for nothing.

Only for you to allow me to love us both enough for the both of us.

Well, that and maybe to stop having so many insecurities.

Genuinely,
Red

1 8 4.

Women are not
territories of conquest,
but since he
discovered her
and settled deep in her roots,
anyone else felt like
an invasion.

Her body was a colony
founded by him.

1 8 5.

A piece of him splintered off and traveled through her
blood stream.
Maybe when they were making love
in that cheap hotel room,
who knows which, there were so many
or maybe in her bed or his or his car or hers
or maybe one of the guest rooms
or on one of the couches or floors
or maybe it was one time he kissed her so hard
on that patio balcony
who knows which
there were so many
or maybe in his shower or hers
or that time they soaked in the tub for hours
But a piece of him punctured a lung
and it was stuck there in her chest
and she feared if it was removed
it would be replaced by a slow leak
so it would remain as a reminder
and as long as she was alive
she would feel him
in every single breath.

Dear Danger,

I used to see it as a curse of sorts — that I can't feel anything for anyone but you. But now I don't see it as short-circuited as much as a wire that was deliberately cut.

A wire that can be taped up with electrical tape to ad nauseam, but the wires cannot be fused back together. Electricity will never flow through again.

You didn't break me, rather than you're on the other end of the only circuit in me that's still intact. And, admittedly, that did feel broken, and it still does at times, but in actuality…

You're the only thing that has ever made me feel whole.

Genuinely,
Red

1 8 6.

Over time,
the greatest evidence
she had found that their souls
were not meeting for the first time
is that they had only slept
on blankets and sleeping bags
or couches or fold out futons
with only enough space
for one person to occupy
and all that separated
their souls
was skin
and the only way
their bodies could rest
is if they shared the same
space
as if it were only occupied
by one.

1 8 7.

She would never
take pieces of him
and make him less than
the more
that she wanted for him.

Dear Danger,

I miss you. And I see you every single day, but God, I miss you. And the passion, and the longing. I miss the desperation and the not being able to et out of my panties fast enough to get you inside me. But I go through the motions and I ride the coaster down the hill as my heart drops into my stomach, until it brings us high again.

Genuinely,
Red

And then there are days
hands hold exactly
what they're meant to
how they're meant to:
belonging to
you
and only you.

1 8 8.

"So, are you officially official yet?"
Is what they ask.

"Because this arbitrary societal
meaningless classification
is the only way I'll know
if what you have
is legitimate and real to me."
Is what she heard.

To answer the question:
Yes, they were official.
Officially happy,
officially the healthiest
human relationship
she'd ever had,
officially the truest of friends
and lovers.
Officially whole and valid
without their judgment
and need to put them
in a pretty box with a pretty bow.

They never would fit in that box,
regardless of how hard it was
for everyone else to understand.
(Oh, so hard for them,
oh, so sad.)

They were not sorry.

I always thought a phoenix
rose from the smoldering
of hard times,
until I saw us rise
from a blazing passion.

And I thought
I would only be satisfied
living inside a flame,
but I'm appreciating the view
from the sky.

Dear Danger,

I was sitting in this bar with you and the one's who made you and thinking about how I used to sit in those same seats, almost a decade ago, with a group that filled at least four tables and pitchers of Long Islands. Those nights always ended in either tears or vomit or both. Another life flashed before my eyes. I tried to focus on you three talking at the same time but the atmosphere and light distracted me.

It was
so much brighter.

Genuinely,
Red

1 8 9.

Her father told her that she loved
a mustang – feral and unbroken
and she told him that it was true.
She could effortlessly love a mare
who would come to any hand.
It was not even the lack of challenge
that deterred her,
as beings are not titles to be won
after a long-fought battle,
but what deterred her was
that they feign love.

And she would ask,
"What is love?
What is a love
that would love anyone?"

She wondered
what was wrong with her
that she didn't want that simple,
easy kind of love.
After all,
they answered her,
"Real love is uncomplicated."

But she would say,
"But what is real?"

It seemed, to her,
unhappy and boring.

She had seen it, she had done it.

But when she loved a mustang,
it was tempestuous and hungry.
And the day he saw her
and his eyes softened,
and he stared at her
longer than before,
it mattered that it was her
and not just anyone.

Day in and day out,
she came to the fence,
with a little kibble in her hand,
and someone, anyone, loving her
was no matter.
Yet, that seemed to be the priority,
for those who loved mares:
to be loved, to find someone
who would love them.

But when one loved a mustang,
they knew that the mustang
very well may never love them
in return,
and that that the mustang
would belong to nothing
but the wind,
and they didn't love them
simply out of hope

that it would change them.

She loved a mustang
because of his unbridled intensity,
she loved him for his wild
and she didn't want to tame it.

So, when they see her riding bareback
in the open fields
and that echo they hear is her laughter
they'll know why
she so foolishly, recklessly, madly
loved a mustang.

Humans are like leaves
blowing in the wind
and they are
as free as the breeze
that carries them
through this life
to the next.

Dear Danger,

My heart rests easy, so easy. Tucked safe in your sheets, kisses on her forehead, pats and squeezes, sweet sprays of spring showers coming through the open window, and a firm grip.

But she remembers, she remembers, secret sobs and sorrows, insecurity, irregularity, an abundance of questions with   unsatisfying open-ended answers, and clamoring to hold on to those strong hands — begging, please, please closer, please closer.

Anxious days, passionate nights, clinging to you so tightly, you'd have to peel her off.

But you patiently stitched time into a calming lullaby and sang her right to sleep, and she re-tained the love she would allow

and everything is different now.

Forever,
Red

1 9 0.

She told her Granny at Thanksgiving
the very first year he came along,
"When you know, you know."

And her Granny replied,
"I guess I've never known."
Her Granny had been married five times
that she would admit.
Her dad told her that it was more like
seven or eight.

She knew.
And what she knew was that he was
who her soul had chosen to love
long before it had chosen a body
to dwell in.

She would love only him in all her lifetimes,
like her Granny's sister
who lost her husband to cancer
in their 40s
and never remarried.

It made her sad that her Granny,
with her Alzheimer's
and borrowed time,
never knew that love.

But it made her believe
that it wasn't easy to come by
at the same time.

And maybe, why it took so long
for someone to see her
is that only pieces of the same star
could recognize the other pieces
of itself
when wrapped in
human skin.

And
when you know,
you know.

1 9 1.

That Christmas
he gave her
secondhand pearls
he'd gotten from
his mother
and lotions and body wash
that came in a pretty box.

She used the box to store
bits and pieces of him:
champagne corks, Topo Chico bottle caps,
notes on hotel paper from everywhere
they had ever stayed,
and she used every drop
of the lotions and body wash.

And sometimes she slept
in the pearls
in case she met him

in dreams
or their next life.

TWENTY SEVEN
EPILOGUE

1 9 2.

It is liberating,
but it is
mostly
absolutely terrifying
that we belong to nothing.
We are alone.

Yet, he discovered
the depths of which
she was unaware existed.
They swam, and they flew,
and they waded
a time or two.

She gave him
the love,
that no one else
had ever seen.

He held her, truly.

He strayed, but never far,
and he always returned
to her.
And, in his own way,
he allowed her to love him
completely
with all of her being.

Her being that
was not his,
or anyone's,
but only sometimes hers.

And, despite having
no obligations to her,
he continued to choose
to share his space with her
in their occupied fragment
of time.

He,
and only he,
(not even she),
saw her
like she had longed
to be seen.

"I suppose, Dear Danger,"
she told him,
"I suppose this woman
you have made of me
is someone else entirely,
and, I suppose, that
she
is sometimes
(and for the rest of her lives)

yours."

But more,
much more
than this,
they did it
their way.

Made in the USA
Lexington, KY
09 January 2019